50 Years of
Dounreay

BY

WILLIAM A. PATERSON

This is an account of the work of the Dounreay Experimental Reactor Establishment in Caithness from its inception until the present day and its impact on the county of Caithness.

Published by
North of Scotland
NEWSPAPERS
Wick, Caithness, Scotland

About the Author

William 'Bill' Paterson is a freelance journalist with a regular column in the John O'Groat Journal. His interest in energy matters hails from his time in industry when, for a number of years, he was responsible for energy matters in a large manufacturing company.

Unless otherwise stated, all the photographs in this book are the copyright © of the Dounreay Site Restoration Ltd.
Additional photographs are reproduced by kind permission of the following:
National Portrait Gallery
and
J McDonald (Photographers) Wick.

ISBN 978-1-871704-37-2

Produced by North of Scotland Newspapers, 42 Union Street, Wick, Caithness, Scotland.

A Catalogue Record of this book is available from the British Library.

Front Cover: Designed by Chris Irwin

Front Endpapers: Cutaway of DFR (Dounreay Fast Reactor)
Back Endpapers: Cutaway of PFR (Prototype Fast Reactor)

FOREWORD

Fifty years, a time of Jubilee; originally a time when debts were cancelled, relationships mended, wrongs righted and things put back as they once were. There is real doubt if the Jubilee ever was more than a pious dream, for we cannot go back, the angel with the flaming sword still bars the way. Yet still this is a time for trumpets, for celebration. This book is dedicated to "all those who have ever worked at Dounreay and who have striven for its cause."

So let us blow the trumpet for all the pioneers, not just the famous and honoured but the thousands of ordinary folk by whose skill and effort the physicists' dream became reality. Pioneers – the word means in French foot soldiers. The Greek equivalent arxegos means author, originator, one who goes where no-one has ever been. Let us sound the ram's horn for those who, and let none gainsay, succeeded in turning swords into ploughshares in fulfilment of another prophetic dream. Oh yes they made mistakes, but the fast reactor they built worked and the spin-off technology has been and will continue to be of enormous benefit as we enter into yet another of our regular "energy crises" periods.

It was on August 6, 1945, the Feast of the Transfiguration, that the first atomic bomb fell on Hiroshima. Those who saw it spoke of a flash "brighter than a thousand suns". Let us blow the trumpets for those who harnessed that same fearsome power for common good.

It has been my privilege as part of the Inter Church Industrial Mission Team to be around Dounreay for the last 22 years, so I am humbly proud to pay my tribute and express my thanks for the friendship and banter, coffee and fellowship I have shared. The challenge for the next generation is the same – to be pioneers, to seek solutions, to take risks, to experiment, to turn dream to reality.

Rev Ronnie Johnstone

From the Table of the Gods

The Story of the Dounreay Experimental Reactor Establishment
In Caithness and its impact on the county of Caithness

Whatever nature has in store for Mankind, unpleasant as it may be, men must accept,
for ignorance is never better than knowledge

Enrico Fermi

Contents

It was Prometheus who stole fire from the table of the gods to give to Mankind.

Prometheus had created Man and was, no doubt, biased in favour of humanity whom the gods had decided served no useful purpose and had failed miserably. In fact, the gods were on the point of ending the experiment. Once Man had fire though, as the wise Prometheus had foreseen (his very name means foresight), there was a shield to protect against the caprices of the gods. Fire permitted Man to eat his food cooked, kept him warm, protected him from wild animals, cleared underbrush to isolate game, prepared fields for cultivation, and allowed the smelting of metals and, hence, the development of tools.

Fire was the beginning of technology.

Yet, history shows that Man was not contented, was never contented with what he had and what he had achieved. Man became aware there was more on the divine table, something there that promised even greater rewards than mere fire alone. This was perpetual fire and this time Man intended to take it from the table of the gods himself –

Caithness: 5,000 years of decommissioning. Na Tri Sithean, a chambered cairn atop Cnoc Freiceadain, overlooking Dounreay. *Reproduced by kind permission of Duncan Kennedy.*

Chapter One
A New Hope

When the war ended – the War, the Second World War that had seen almost the whole world erupt in flames – it was a time of relief, a time for rejoicing, but it was also an anxious time, still a time of tension. The aims of the Allies had been but partly achieved. The evil of Hitler and the Nazis and their mindless cruelty were gone and fascism had retreated; but yet the world was such that more men lived under authoritarian regimes than lived under liberal democracies. And it was a new world; a world difficult to understand. Churchill had rightly stated that an iron curtain had been drawn across the continent as the rigid and corrupt bureaucracy of totalitarian Communism spread across the old countries of eastern and middle Europe. Throughout the world the giant powers of the United States of America and the Soviet Union faced each other as rivals in a strange new form of hostility that came to be termed the 'Cold War.'

Perhaps what stopped this muted aggression from breaking into all-out world war anew was the astonishing development of weaponry that the war had spawned and, in particular, the advancement of the nuclear arsenal. Robert Oppenheimer, the leading scientist associated with the development of the atom bomb, was stunned by the awesome power of the first trial atomic explosion in the desert of New Mexico. Oppenheimer, with his classical background, could only rationalise it in the lines from Bhagavad-Gita, the Hindu scripture, 'I am become death: the destroyer of worlds.'

In truth the first atom bomb tested released very little energy compared to that of an average thunderstorm or the energy daily exerted by sunshine as it casually lifts millions of tons of water high into the atmosphere: but what was unique about the explosion that Oppenheimer witnessed was that an immense concentration of energy had been contained in a very small package and let loose in an incredibly short time, a minute fraction of a second. This weapon proved its power at Hiroshima and Nagasaki where over 200,000 died almost immediately and more were to die in the weeks, months and years that followed as a result of the poorly understood effects of radiation poisoning.

But if the bomb was terrifying the energy that the bomb demonstrated also brought a hope. The need for such an intensity of energy is rare. It is the quantity available that is the concern, not the rapidity of its discharge and, in our economic world, the all-important cost of obtaining that energy. The splitting of the atom gave men dreams to dream; the peaceful and controlled use of nuclear energy as a virtually unlimited and inexpensive form of fuel beckoned. Indeed, back in the heady days of the fifties of the last century, some scientists (notably R.M.Langer, a physicist at the California Institute of Technology) even considered nuclear power would produce electricity so cheaply it would not be worth charging for. There was talk of nuclear powered motorcars, aeroplanes, and even cigarette lighters.

The essential building blocks for the peaceful uses of nuclear energy had actually been in place since before the war. The Italian physicist Enrico Fermi had won a Nobel Prize in 1938 for his research and experiments with radioactive materials. No lover of fascism, he used the permission given to him by Italy's fascist government to attend the award ceremony in Sweden to flee with his family to the United States.

Aware that German scientists were also researching this field and concerned of the danger if Hitler and his Nazis had such a power at their disposal, Fermi and a group of his fellow physicists composed a letter to President Franklin D. Roosevelt spelling out the possibility. The letter was signed by one Albert Einstein and delivered through an intermediary to the President. The ultimate result was the Manhattan Project – the project for

the manufacture of an atom bomb – as the Allies strove to master this new power before Hitler's Germany grasped what was happening.

Fermi was entrusted with a key role in the development of a self-sustaining nuclear chain reaction. It took place in December 1942, in a small reactor which Fermi termed an 'atomic pile.' This had been assembled in a makeshift laboratory under the stands of a football field at the University of Chicago. Fermi later stated he had meant to disparage it by the name 'pile' and that he should really have called it a heap – but the name stuck. The safety control rod for the experiment was made of cadmium and was attached to a rope over a pulley and suspended over the reactor. Should anything have gone wrong it was the task of a designated scientist to cut the rope with an axe, thereby dropping the cadmium rod into the reactor such that the rod would, it was fervently hoped, then absorb enough neutrons to stop the reaction.

The scientist with this task was, jokingly, referred to as the Safety Control Rod Axe Man and ever since then any emergency shutdown of such a plant has been called a 'SCRAM.'

Soon after Fermi's successful experimental operation, plans were drawn up for a series of nuclear power plants. The first production reactor went into action at the Hanford site in Richland, Washington, in September 1944. There had been friction between America and Britain over the sharing of this technology with America abruptly ceasing to provide information to Britain and Canada. Although the reasons for this were complex and not down to one sole reason, America did believe, rightly as it turned out, that communist sympathisers had penetrated the British intelligence and scientific communities and were feeding the Soviet Union with details of the technology. The British physicist (born German) Klaus Fuchs was later sentenced to fourteen years for spying for the Soviet Union. This sudden withdrawing of co-operation forced Britain to act on her own. British and Canadian scientists had contributed significantly to the Manhattan Project however and there was an awareness of what was required.

Initially the main thrust was into the manufacture of the prestigious atom bomb and facilities were set up to develop this; 'We have got to have this thing over here whatever it costs,' said the Foreign Secretary, Ernest Bevin, 'We've got to have the bloody Union Jack on top of it.'

There were other reasons for the development of nuclear power. There was an awareness that the country's indigenous coal supplies would not last forever and that importing of foreign fuels would add to the balance of payments problems as well being less secure.

So it was that John Cockcroft (1897-1967), the physicist who was later to win a Nobel Prize for his pioneering work in 'splitting' the atom, was appointed to head up the British nuclear effort. In 1946, Cockcroft, later Sir John, set up the Harwell Atomic Energy Research Establishment using an old war time airfield some 16 miles south of Oxford and, a year after that, the first British reactor went into operation. It produced 100-kilowatts and ran with a graphite moderator on uranium metal fuel. Nicknamed 'GLEEP' (for Graphite Low Energy Experimental Plant) this was to run for a remarkable 43 years. After this reactor had started a series of others followed in short succession, all with less than romantic acronymic names such as BEPO, DIDO, and PLUTO.

Three months after Cockcroft's appointment another was made; this related to the establishment of an organisation at Risley in Lancashire intended to produce fissile material as a fuel and brought Christopher Hinton (1901 -

Sir John Cockcroft.

The first four light bulbs lit from atomic power.
Reproduced by kind permission of Idaho National Laboratory.

1983), another remarkable man (later Lord Hinton of Bankside) who had been ICI's chief engineer, into the nuclear industry. In 1951 Hinton was instrumental in setting up the Fast Reactor Design Committee. Although an earlier committee had considered other options the fast reactor was envisaged as the answer to the long-term demand for power because of its ability to breed fuel and thus be self-sustaining in fissile material. Trials with ZEPHYR, a low power fast reactor had led in turn to ZEUS – a reactor which proved the concept and which pointed to the next stage of a larger experimental fast reactor that would generate more meaningful power supplies.

The Americans were first however in producing usable electricity from atomic power. At the National Reactor Testing Station in Idaho four light bulbs strung across a railing in the turbine room of fast reactor EBR 1 lit up on December the 20th of 1951 to herald in a new age. Britain was not far behind; indeed, it could be argued that, in some ways, even in front. A separate corporation had been set up in 1954 to oversee all atomic energy projects; this was the United Kingdom Atomic Energy Authority (UKAEA) and it was under the aegis of this body (the Design Committee became absorbed in it) that Hinton supervised the construction of Calder Hall in Cumbria, the world's first large-scale nuclear power plant to feed into a commercial grid. It opened in 1956. But, before that, Hinton had become involved in something else: something that was going to hurl a remote and peaceful Highland community into a turbulence that was to put it at the cutting edge of science and technology.

Graphite Low Energy Experimental Plant (GLEEP).

'Winter Scene' by local artist Frank Begg.
Reproduced by kind permission of the artist.

The Caithness landscape with Morven and Scaraben in the background.
Reproduced by kind permission of Studiograff.

Chapter Two
The Far North

Thurso reminds one of a painting by Pieter Brueghal the Younger. As you approach it along the long sweep of the Causewaymire (the road through the peat lands of Caithness) the town suddenly bursts upon you. Medieval with its many sizes and shapes of buildings and variegated and various roof tops (and even more obviously so when they are picked out by snow), the Brueghal comparison soon disappears when you stand on the promenade overlooking Thurso beach and view out to the misty and mystical Orkneys. Then it can only be a Turner seascape you are appreciating as the fugitive mists and colours now reveal and then conceal; a sparkle of sun and the dramatic changes to the quietly beautiful.

Caithness, where Thurso sits, is the Scottish mainland's most northerly county. A small land, it covers less than 700 square miles and faces the Atlantic Ocean and the Pentland Firth on its north side and the North Sea on its east coast. It is basically a sandstone based plateau covered in rich peat sloping from the high metamorphic quartzite hills of the south – Morven soars 2313 feet and the highest of the three Scarabens challenges it at only 250 feet less – to the alluvial plains of the north and north-east and ending in an almost continuous line of high cliffs, some as high as 400 feet. In the middle lies the famed flow country, largely bog speckled with small lochs and drained by streams, which is home to a unique and varied flora and a rich wildlife. Few trees grow in the county, other than in certain sheltered areas, largely due to the biting winds and the proximity to the sea. Indeed, it is because the all embracing sea scarves the land that Caithness enjoys a temperate climate and the Gulf Stream ensures the worst wrath of winter is assuaged.

The county is rich in historic remains dating from Neolithic times onwards. As the great glaciers of the last Ice Age made their snarling retreat, grinding and scarring the land as they did so, men pushed north and settled in the sheltered glens marked out by the ice. The standing stones and chambered cairns (the cairns up to 230 feet long by 50 feet wide and around 11 feet in height) testify to the people of the time and their agrarian and peaceful civilisation. There were more trees about then as the remains of old buildings testify – banks of earth with wooden lintels and timber roofing. We know these people farmed, growing cereal crops such as barley and oats and that they had cattle, goats and, inevitably, sheep. This was to set a pattern that was to last down the centuries.

If the first people to settle were peaceful, from around 1000 B.C. successive immigrants were less so. The horse reached Caithness and with it wheeled vehicles. The plough came and so did advanced metal tools. Times were more turbulent and the mysterious rounded brochs (sometimes named 'duns') appeared. These were multi-purpose buildings, tall towers with internal wooden floors that served as look-out posts, living quarters, defensive forts (most had ditches around them), grain stores, cattle barns, and – surely – party zones. They generally appeared wherever the land was being cultivated during the Iron Age. The majority have been dated to around 100 B.C. to 200 A.D. although usage of brochs may have extended from 500 B.C. to as late as 500 A.D. A significant one – significant to this story – was erected on the north coast and surrounded by earthen works or 'rath' as it was called. Colloquially this Dunrath became Dounreay.

Then came the Vikings. When they arrived, mainly from the new Viking colony of Orkney, they came as much as settlers as fiery conquerors and they were to leave an indelible mark on the county. Unruly they may have been at first but if they had settled on the land, in turn they were settled by the land. They named its features and set up their fiefdoms. Slowly

The Grey Cairns of Camster, excavated and partially rebuilt in the 1980s.

hamlets grew and villages formed and roads, rough and ready, crossed the flow country where people hacked out the ready peat for fuel. At this time, Caithness was linked organisationally with the Orkney Islands and common rulers are recorded for both. Norse names abound around the coast, especially the north coast facing the Orkneys. Place names such as Freswick, Huna, Scrabster and Seater all testify to Viking settlement and influence. 'Caithness' for the Vikings, was 'Katanes' the 'headland of the cat people,' although the county was also named in Irish annuals as 'Cait.' Wick was the first town – it was mentioned in the Sagas as 'Vik,' a word meaning a bay or a haven. And then there was Thurso, 'Thor's River' in honour of that thunderous God. The Vikings were well established in Thurso by 900 A.D. as they sat at the mouth of the river in the shelter of the bay.

But even by then Caithness was already known to the Scottish kings and, early in the new millennium, something of their writ ran. A judicious policy of playing one side off against the other as disputes erupted over land gradually weaned Caithness away from Norwegian influence and put it under Scottish central control. After the Battle of Largs in 1263 where the Scots' army defeated a Norwegian force, Scottish rule was well established. A map of Caithness from this time shows Wick, a mere 'huddle of turf huts,' as the main settlement in the county.

Civilisation crept in slowly. In 1496 one Jan de Groot, a Dutchman, gained the franchise to ferry passengers from the place now named after him (John O' Groats) to the Orkneys. It is possible that the Groat coin also gained its name from him, as this was the rate fixed to control prices for the crossing. A few years later, in 1503, Wick was awarded the dignity of a sheriff court and, in 1589, was granted the Royal Charter that afforded it the protection of the crown and gained it valuable trading rights.

Thurso also had progressed. St. Peter's Church, initially built in the 13th Century and matching Sweetheart Abbey of Dumfriesshire in its simple attractiveness, was renovated around the early 1600's and Thurso castle was erected in 1660 by George, the Earl of Caithness.

This followed Thurso being made a free burgh in 1633, an event that provided the town with some of the trading advantages enjoyed by Wick and reflected its growing importance as a point of trade with Scandinavia and the Baltic countries. 'The granary of Scandinavia' Caithness had been called with a little pardonable exaggeration as it exported its fast ripening barley (termed 'bere') to those lands. The importance of the Netherlands to Thurso was, and is, reflected in Rotterdam Street in the town centre. Most of Thurso's bustling trade came from the export of fish, skins, and grains and it imported wine, timber and salt. The town could even boast ownership of two sloops. In 1735 Aeneas Bayne wrote of Thurso, 'It is a neat little fashionable town.' Later, in the same century, the first commercial quarrying of flagstones began (by a Mr. Scott of Murkle). However, it was James Traill who really established the industry in the 1820's and by 1825 the first export orders were leaving Thurso for abroad. At its peak, the quarrying industry in Caithness was second only to that of Aberdeenshire.

Around this time the population of Thurso was about 3,000 whereas Wick numbered some 1,500 but something was stirring for Wick. In the cold, dark waters of the North Sea Clupea Harengus was swarming in silvery shoals.

The herring industry was what made Wick and reverberated all around the county and the country and even put Wick into international prominence. In less than fifty years some 30,000 persons could be found in Wick's streets during the height of the fishing season and the British Fisheries Society had begun building a new town on Wick's boundary (Pulteneytown) designed by no less a person than Thomas Telford.

The county as a whole gained by this enormous boom as Wick became the leading herring fishing port in Europe (later Wick and Pulteneytown were to unite). The spin-off industries proved equally important – net and rope making, coopering, shipping and carting. There was also a substantial rise in building within the county as hotels and lodging houses rose like daffodils in spring.

Thurso remained behind however, its population seemingly fixed at a little over 3,000. As a port, it served the eight nearby quarries as Caithness flagstones went out into the world in the 19th century. Its fishers went

Old St Peter's Church.

Herring Drifters in Wick Harbour.

Thurso Castle, seen from the Thurso River.

forth also; not, as Wick, for herring but mainly for white fish; and Thurso remained, what it had always been, the centre of its own farming community; a community that came into town every Tuesday for market day. Most of the farms were small, barely more than crofts if not so, and living was scarcely above subsistence.

The first world war expanded horizons as the sons of Thurso and Caithness left for far places and new people poured in – generally naval personnel concerned with the Fleet based at Scapa Flow in the Orkneys. After that, and after that great sacrifice (over 1,000 were killed from Caithness out of a total population of only a little over 40,000) Thurso went into quiet decline as the great days of white fishing began to fade and the flagstone industry, the industry that had paved the Strand and had employed over 1,000 in its high years, suffered from the ever fiercer competition from concrete pavements and concrete paving stones.

The second world war saw another massive upheaval in the traditional way of life. Again thousands thronged through the county. Caithness became cosmopolitan as members of the armed forces from all around the world came into it. There were even German and Italian prisoners of war who would work in the fields (and happily return for holidays in quieter times) and there was an army of Irish immigrant workers as well as a battalion of Polish servicemen stationed on the airfield at Dounreay. Wick was the first town in Britain to be bombed in daylight by the Luftwaffe but again Caithness came through with dignity and having more than done its duty.

But, by 1951, the decline in Caithness was evident. Population had sunk to 22,710 according to that year's census (about half the permanent population of the mid-1800's) and this was skewed towards the elderly and very young by the dearth of 16 to 24 year olds as that age group were forced south for work. Fishing and flagstones were both slowly dying and even the other 'F,' farming, was mechanising swiftly and not providing the

job opportunities that it once had. In truth, the waning of agriculture as regards employment could be traced back to the early 19th Century when new breeds of sheep had been introduced and people had been forced out of their homes to make way. The grim statistic that underscored all this economic rundown in the 1950's was the 17.8% winter jobless figure in the Thurso Bureau of Employment. The deterioration was evident in Caithness; and Thurso, in the words of Caithness writer Donald Omand, was heading 'into little more than a beautiful village.'

And then a determined man spotted an opportunity.

Aerial view of Wick from the north, with the harbour and Pulteneytown shown top centre.

Sir David Robertson by Bassano.

Chapter Three
A Gathering of Eagles

Sir David Robertson has the distinction of having his photograph held on file in the National Portrait Gallery. Taken by Bassano, in its sombre greys it reflects something of the tough, intelligent, passionate, tenacious and outspoken individual that was Sir David.

He was born in Glasgow (in 1890) although he came from good Caithness stock. His grandfather had been headmaster of Stirkoke School in the county. His father, John Robertson, had moved south however to progress his career and, ultimately, had become the Chief Inspector of the General Post Office. Young David attended the noted Allan Glen's School and from there entered Glasgow University. Upon leaving he was apprenticed to a well-known Glasgow accountancy firm of the day, Mitchell and Smith but, ever ambitious, moved on to the larger Staff, Cole, Dickens and Hall in 1912.

The first World War saw him volunteering in 1915 and from the Glasgow University Officer Training Corp he enlisted with the Argyll and Sutherland Highlanders and joined with the British Expeditionary Force to France.

Invalided out after being severely wounded, he was attached to the Ministry of Food as sectional accountant, 'Fish, Game, Poultry and Eggs Section.' He attended the Armistice in France as the chief accountant to the Ministry.

After the war he entered the fishing and cold storage industries and soon became managing director of several companies. He was married by now and, by the time he entered politics, had two daughters. In 1939 he won the constituency of Streatham in London for the Conservative Party. He was knighted for his war work in 1945.

But politics is a strange business. Sir David held a solid Conservative seat in the heart of London not far from where he had made his home. His motives for leaving such a position to fight the remote and highly marginal constituency of Caithness and Sutherland have always been a matter of speculation. He would have known that Caithness was a strong Liberal area stemming from the time when the Liberals were identified with the policy of crofting law reform. By and large the landowning class represented Caithness in Parliament whilst the business class ran local affairs. Since the end of the war, however, the Conservative and Unionist Party had held the county by their fingertips. This may have been an attraction to Sir David who had always loved a good fight. Perhaps, more prosaically, he thought that by representing Caithness he could get more time for his hobbies of fishing and golfing.

It is unlikely that he would have moved, however, had not the prominent Conservative Sir Duncan Sandys, son-in-law of Winston Churchill, been looking for a safe Conservative seat in order to re-enter the Commons after his defeat in the 1945 general election. Doubtless Sir David was glad to make way for him and to pursue his own career in that strange country that he only knew from the tales his father had told him when he was a boy. Sir David himself always claimed he felt drawn to the land of his ancestors and perhaps it was so; a land far removed from the bustle of the gas-lit Glasgow of the turn of the century that he had grown up in with its crowded streets and horse drawn trams and endless noise.

Typically, Sir David threw himself into his new role with enthusiasm after winning the constituency in the 1950 general election by a slim majority of 269 votes (but that was an increase of 263 over the last incumbent's majority). Sir David poured his boundless energy into raising the prospects for the area he represented. He quickly analysed the situation and saw

the general decline of the counties of the far north and the running down of their traditional industries. He knew the area needed work and he tried his best to re-establish brickworks in Brora and even attempted to keep something of the Brora coalmine going by investing some of his own money into the enterprise. He was always generously inclined, delighting the Caithness London Association by his contribution of toys at the children's Christmas party.

Then, in the House of Commons on a late January day in 1953, Sir David heard his friend Duncan Sandys, then Minister for Supply, make a short statement that was to send him into a fever of frenzied activity that was to end up changing the face of his constituency for ever.

The statement that Duncan Sandys made on that day was in reply to a question that had been submitted a few days before concerning the government's plans to raise electrical power from atomic energy. Contained in his reply Sandys made two points that Sir David latched onto. Sandys said in connection with atomic energy, 'If the prospects are shown to be favourable, we shall consider constructing an experimental atomic power station of this kind,' and he added, 'we are at present looking for a suitable site to construct this plant.' He meant by experimental power station of this kind a natural uranium fast reactor and Sir David immediately knew where a suitable site for the project was.

In truth, Sir David may already have had an inkling of what was to happen before Sandys' statement but, in any event, it did not take him long to contact Sandys afterwards; and, after all, Sandys did owe him a political favour. He repaid it by guiding Sir David to Christopher Hinton.

Hinton was a tall (almost 6 feet 6 inches), languid man of distinguished and even aristocratic bearing. He was eleven years younger than Sir David and had come from a comfortable background, emerging from Trinity College, Cambridge, with a first class honours in mechanical engineering. He had ultimately joined Imperial Chemical Industries (ICI) in the same year as he had married. He soon had risen to the post of chief engineer. When war broke out he entered the Ministry of Supply and took on the role of deputy-general of filling factories. This brought him directly into the production of ammunition and weapons and, after the War, he progressed into atomic power eventually becoming the managing director (Industrial Group) United Kingdom Atomic Energy Authority. It was in this capacity that he was seeking a site for his experimental atomic power plant. Later, he was to become the chairman of the Central Electricity Generating Board. Amongst this man's many – and they were many – honours, he was to become a knight in 1951 and a Fellow of the Royal Society in 1954. He was made one of the first life peers in 1965 and the following year gained the Imperial Order of the Rising Sun from Japan!

What this intellectual man whose work was his hobby thought of the more emotional and volatile Sir David we cannot be certain. He would certainly respect him and appreciate his intelligence but he may have been quietly amused at his more outgoing and extravagant companion.

As a result of Sir David's pleas and, possibly, at the pressing of Sandys, Hinton found himself on the platform of Inverness station meeting up again with Sir David after having stepped from the overnight sleeper from London. We know better what Hinton and his travelling companion James Kendall, the chief engineer (fast reactors) for what was to become the UKAEA, had breakfasted on than what they were thinking. No doubt wondering what kind of world they were coming to and when they were

Christopher Hinton.

likely to get food again they had plied themselves well with kippers, bacon and egg, sausages and beans. On the chauffeured drive north, Sir David was dismayed to learn that Hinton had already had reports on potential sites in the far north from surveyors and that those reports had not been very favourable. He was also dampened to discover a factor that he had not considered and that was the reactor's potential hazard to local civilian populations if anything went wrong; an event that, although unlikely, had to be considered.

The rest of the day did not go too well either. Hinton met up with the county architect, William Wilson, and with the editor of the local paper (the John O'Groat Journal), David Oag. Hinton made it clear what he was looking for; a 400 acre flat site on low lying ground with easy access to the sea and with copious amounts of fresh water available (Dounreay is close to Lochs Calder and Shurrery). The site had to lie solidly on rock and had to be far enough away from centres of population in case of any accidents but, paradoxically, near enough them to provide a large workforce and all the amenities that such would require. Another unspoken factor was that it had to be relatively secure in the event of a major war breaking out again.

They viewed six sites that day in a short time. Dounreay was last on their list and Sir David had higher hopes of this than the others. Certainly Hinton spent more time at Dounreay. Yet he was non-committal and he still had to view sites in Sutherland. 'We are just taking a look round,' was all he said to the Groat as he departed.

In fact he had probably made up his mind. Not only did Dounreay fit most of the requirements but also, fortuitously, the Admiralty was already entrenched there with their wartime airfield that included hangars and other buildings and thus much of the required infrastructure was already in place. There would be less hassle and delay in setting up. Importantly, Thurso Town Council still controlled its own planning authority. Decisions concerning the town would be quick. A further point was that all the local people that were aware of the reason for the visit were enthusiastic for the plant, which was not the case in other areas Hinton had been to.

One other issue played a part. The political fact was that the constituency was a marginal and it could do nothing but good for the Conservative cause if the plant were placed in Caithness. Hinton could not weigh this factor in his personal assessment but it would not be discounted elsewhere.

There followed a period of anxious waiting. The strain must have been greatest on Sir David who had put so much effort into it all and who stood to lose credibility should his efforts prove in vain. He was not kept in suspense for long. He was told sometime before the First of March of 1954 when Sir David Eccles, then Minister for Works, made the formal statement in the House of Commons. Dounreay was the site chosen. Atomic energy was coming to Caithness.

Sir David's triumph was not his alone; a fact that he was always careful to stress. Men such as Brigadier George David Keith Murray,

Brigadier George David Keith Murray. (copyright J MacDonald, Wick).

convenor of Caithness County Council (later to be Lord Lieutenant of the County) and John Sinclair, Provost of Thurso (and also to become Lord Lieutenant of the County), had more than played their part. The full value of these individuals would be seen later as they eased the way for the new plant to root satisfactorily. At well over six feet John Sinclair was an imposing individual and, like the Brigadier, made the United Kingdom Atomic Energy Authority welcome without ever compromising his own position which was, constantly, to ensure that the welfare and benefit of the community was taken into account.

John Sinclair (right) with Provost William Dunnett of Wick.

If there were any objections to the plant, they were well muted. The high unemployment figure and the long trodden road south that the youngsters took in search of work overrode all.

The main credit of course was Sir David's and he took full advantage of that – and quite rightly so. Sir David's future hopes for the plant and the area proved misplaced in the long run. He envisaged other industries springing up around the atomic plant. 'The people in the north of Scotland – will realise that, perhaps, a new era is beginning and that the old one, which depopulated the Highlands, is ending. I believe it heralds the second industrial revolution. The first one passed us by because of our lack of coal.'

Sir David had based his beliefs on his early observations that, wherever electricity-producing plants had been built, this had attracted manufacturers to that area. It was not to be so in the case of Caithness. Partly this was due to improvements at the time in the reduction of transmission losses that were involved in sending electricity through cables over long distances and partly because of the spread of the national grid system that ensured electricity was readily available all over the British Isles. This lessened the dependency of manufacturers to be near the point of production of power. It was also because of the very nature of the Dounreay establishment itself; its primary function was not to produce power but to experiment with the means of producing power and all the ramifications involved with that. And there was the age-old problem for Caithness, its sheer distance from the heavily populated areas.

But, at least, whatever else developed the nuclear energy experimental plant was coming. Even his political opponents had to admire Sir David and he held his seat with continuously increased majorities. In 1959 his honesty led him to break with the Conservative Parliamentary Party and stand as an independent because he believed the government were not doing enough for the Highlands. He won the seat again of course and was cheered by his enthusiastic supporters. In 1963 he had the honour of becoming the first freeman of Thurso – 'Because of his moral courage, determination to see justice done and his championing of the small man against authority which so easily got intoxicated with itself.' Sir David received a cheque on this occasion and, typically, he added generously to the amount before passing it on to charity. He held back a small portion though to purchase a painting of the county – naturally featuring Dounreay. He died at his Surrey home in 1970.

Chapter Four
Taking to the Sky

Sir David's dream rapidly began to take concrete form (literally concrete).

The United Kingdom Atomic Energy Authority was set up formally in July 1954 with Sir Edwin Plowden as its chairman and with its industrial group under Sir Christopher Hinton.

There was now a multitude of activities to be carried out – and all at once. This was in the days when network analysis, as a tool to manage projects, was still in its infancy and computer control was unheard of. Much had to be done by pencil, rubber and slide rule.

Aerial view of the Dounreay airfield showing at the top, Boston camp and the individual sleeping quarters.

The first physical signs were slight. Surveyors of the advance party arrived and set up in the control tower of the airfield and began making their measurements and organising the drilling of test boreholes. Negotiations had opened between the UKAEA and the landowners for the purchase of the land around Dounreay on both sides of the A836 as that road wended its way west from Thurso into the hillier country of Sutherland. These discussions were not too difficult since the Admiralty and the Board of Agriculture owned much of the land. Rumours that the Government was buying up farms in the area in case foreign agents purchased them were certainly untrue. The Air Ministry was however keen to retain the airstrip facility in light of the perceived Soviet threat and a suitable deal with the Admiralty was soon achieved.

The young Alistair Fraser, a boy at the time attending Miller Academy and someone who was destined to make a positive mark on both the county and at Dounreay (he became a councillor and eventually was to work in the nuclear plant), remembered passing by the fields and wondering what was going on at the old airfield. He sensed a suppressed excitement in the county and there were whispers of great things in store. He heard that the total cost of the undertaking was expected to exceed £5 million (the actual figure voted by Parliament was £15 million); a sum he concedes is regularly won on the lottery every week in these days but back then was unheard of. The county was certainly stimulated. Thurso Town Council took the decision to build a new secondary school but baulked at funding new houses; it would put all of one shilling and nine pence on the rates (about 9 new pence today – but quite a sum then) and the Town Council decided instead to request that the Atomic Energy Authority finance the project (in the event the Scottish Special Housing Authority helped as well). The Caithness Constabulary did agree, however, to take on four extra policemen and a sergeant for Thurso as well as recruiting another typist. A further two constables were allocated to cover the Dounreay area. As a sign of the times at a dance in the nearby village of Reay sixteen-year-old Miss Margaret Gunn was elected Atomic Queen (fifty years later her husband was to be Chairman of the Dounreay Stakeholders Group).

The appointment of Donald Carmichael as liaison officer (later works' secretary of Dounreay) proved particularly inspired. Donald had been brought up in Reay (the village not two miles from Dounreay). He was a

REQUISITIONED FARM

The farm of Lower Dounreay was one of the best arable units in Caithness when the Ministry of Defence requisitioned it during the second world war. It belonged to Jack Davidson, an officer in the local TA unit, who was called up as a major and earned the Distinguished Service Order for his part in the North Africa campaign. He was killed in Sicily in 1943.

The farmhouse was absorbed into the new nuclear research facility and played a number of roles. In 2003, it was deemed an obstruction for the construction of the new plant needed to empty the site waste shaft and consequently demolished. A plaque made from a roof slate was used to mark the official opening in 2003 of a new central office block for the site. Jack Davidson's daughter, Margaret, and Morris Pottinger, another previous owner of the farm, carried out the opening.

Lower Dounreay Farmhouse.

son of the manse and had been Cambridge educated. He had enjoyed a successful career in the Ministry of Works before being seconded to the Ministry of Supplies' Atomic Energy section. A worldly-wise individual, Donald loved the outdoor life and would rather be out on a site than sit at his desk. He was a cyclist, a rugby player, and became instrumental in re-establishing Reay Golf Club. His first task was to interview and appoint suitable people for the various administrative roles that would be required but, very rapidly, he became the de facto ambassador of the Authority in and for Caithness. His diplomatic skills much in evidence, Donald dealt with tenancy agreements (the Authority had purchased some 1,000 acres but re-let 800 back – most to the

Donald Carmichael.

original farming owners), decided upon suitable premises to convert into a staff hostel, aided with the proposed planned housing scheme to be built in Thurso for the expected influx of workers, and coped with a vast variety of problems that such an undertaking inevitably generated.

It was he who developed the Dounreay Concession Scheme designed to help attract staff to what many then saw as a remote part and it was also he who suggested that Christopher Hinton explain something of the nature of the work and atomic theory to the local people. Carmichael saw the need to involve individuals and to be as open with them as possible. Hinton readily agreed and, as a result, found himself (with his wife this time as well) once again in Caithness on a chilly day early in January.

On the morning of the fourth he was sitting on a table swinging his legs in the cold and damp Operations Room of the aerodrome control tower where the Ministry had earlier set up its headquarters. Hinton's audience was the local crofters and people who would be neighbours of the UKAEA. Later, in the evening (together with Lord Thurso), he faced a tougher meeting when he spoke at Thurso Town Hall to a packed house. By repute there were over 500 in the Hall and more on the stairs – and there were others outside who simply could not get in. Provost John Sinclair presided and Sir Christopher, armed with a long pointer to indicate the detail on the coloured slides being shown, gave a lucid account of atomic power and nuclear reactors. His straightforwardness won the audience and his stating that he had fallen in love with Thurso since it reminded him of his home village in Wiltshire helped as well. 'Clearly,' he said, 'only the fact that we consider there is a remote risk would cause us to build a factory in a remote area like this.' But he did point out that the nuclear industry had a low accident rate compared to the electrical and engineering ones. He then went on to explain that Dounreay had been chosen because it was felt it would cause the least amount of disturbance to build there. He also covered the scale of the risk (potential release of radiation rather than an explosion) and gave reassurances on the effects of the nuclear station on fish and other wildlife. As Alistair Fraser was to put it much later, 'Without realising it, Sir Christopher had undertaken UKAEA's first stakeholder meeting and had secured a very positive outcome.'

But it says much about mankind that the first item erected on the site was an 'unclimbable' fence.

FORTUITOUS LANDING

The Dounreay airfield and control tower never saw combat action during the war. An unsubstantiated story existed of a lone Spitfire pilot once making an emergency landing. This tale was told a visitor to the site exhibition, which was set up in the tower in 1960, by its manager, George Plummer. The visitor replied: "That's right – it was me."

In the face of George's understandable scepticism the visitor abruptly left, went to his car and brought in his old RAF log book to prove the claim. Apparently, flying his Spitfire from Dalcross, he had run out of fuel and, seeing the brand new airfield below, couldn't believe his luck and decided to land.

The Dounreay Control Tower.

Trying to get Caithness on the move again – winter 1955.

Ferrying an emergency to hospital as part of the relief effort.

Chapter Five
Snow and the Camp

By early 1955 all looked in place to begin the hard physical work. The land on the south side of the A836 was being set up to become the 'Camp' for contractors' workforces and some of the UKAEA staff; the intention was, in fact, to utilise the existing Nissen huts and other small buildings that had been maintained there as part of the aerodrome since wartime but, before anything serious could happen, nature displayed another of her powers.

The first snows came at lunchtime on January 12th. Heavy falls turned quickly to blizzards as winds whipped up to 60 miles per hour. For ten long days this weather was to batter Caithness during which the county was virtually cut off. Roads had been quickly blocked and cars and lorries lay abandoned. A train became trapped at Altnabreac on the way to Caithness and the relief train also suffered the same fate. Emergency supplies had to be flown to the passengers.

Six aircraft, an Anson and five support helicopters, operated around the clock ferrying in food and taking injured and ill people out of the county. The frigate 'Urchin' arrived in Wick Bay bringing in petrol and other essential materials. The relief effort was termed 'Operation Snowdrop.' And, just as things were returning to normal, the snows came back with even more severity.

Again the services were called in to help as power lines crashed and people and buses became stranded as snow drifted over thirty feet high in places. An aircraft from Orkney was grounded at Wick with 23 people on board. Even the fire engine sent to help it became trapped. Finally the engine did reach the plane, a Dakota, and attached itself to it to hold it steady until snowploughs arrived to end the five hour long ordeal of the passengers.

Although seven died during the storms, the worst was over by the beginning of March and the work on the site could then commence. The contractors and Ministry men who had arrived from the south took some convincing that the winters were not always so severe and that they had simply witnessed an aberration. Wisely, Donald Carmichael, aware that Caithness was being termed 'Siberia' by the men involved, applied to the Meteorological Office for statistics on Caithness weather which demonstrated that the climate of the far north of Scotland was much like the rest of the country: hard to convince people sitting in candlelight, huddling to keep warm.

Boston Camp winter and summer (reproduced by kind permission of Brian Hart).

The camp – frequently referred to as 'Boston Camp' after the main group of buildings there (all the groups had been named after world war two aircraft) – itself provided only very basic comfort for the first few workers who came in between the January and February falls of snow. Although they were wind and weather tight, the huts required a good deal of decorative and restorative work.

Kitchen amenities had been upgraded and a new dining room added. Facilities were still spartan though. The refurbished sleeping quarters were on the style of the old Nightingale wards with their long line of iron beds, each accompanied with a table and a locker, that could be folded up during the day. The heating of these quarters was provided by pot bellied stoves that harked straight back to their original designer, Benjamin Franklin of American Independence fame, and these were also used for drying clothes set around them thus ensuring the atmosphere was redolent of an overloaded laundrette. Thick, brown linoleum was the only floor covering and though some of the huts were fortunate enough to have communal toilets attached others depended on the outside toilet block. The main contractors for this renovation work were Alexander Hall and Company, an Aberdeen firm who undertook the building work, and James Scott & Company of Perth who were electrical contractors. Even the canteen and the sick bay were renewed. There was also a recreational area and a small camp cinema.

The site accommodation for staff was better than that for the labour force. What had been the officers' quarters were reserved for the management both of the contractors and the Authority (the United Kingdom Atomic Energy Authority that is). Staff enjoyed a room to themselves and there were rugs on floors. There was also a communal lounge with easy chairs and a radiogram in the corner. Most of the senior employees were lodged in Thurso itself though. Ormlie Lodge, in the town, had been purchased and was in the process of being extended to fit the needs of the Authority staff.

The new blocks built by Alexander Hall and Company for the workers were an improvement being built in an 'H' pattern with two rows of four-bedded rooms separated by a corridor, and with toilet and washing facilities, including the luxury of showers, in the linking section.

As the work force from the main contractors arrived – Whatlings of Glasgow had won the main contract and the Motherwell Bridge Company was to fabricate the sphere – feeding this army became a major undertaking. By the end of April of 1955 over four hundred lived on the site. Eventually the camp came to have a population of over two thousand people. To cope with this, butchers, bakers, cooks, kitchen assistants all worked around the clock. Without modern amenities, all food had to be prepared from the constant influx of fresh meat, sacks of sugar, flour, and vegetables. Tea and butter arrived in foil lined wooden boxes and bread was delivered every second day from Inverness. Milk came in churns from the dairy farm at Scrabster – a village along the coast from Thurso. Indeed, vans and vehicles were turning up with provisions of one sort or another on a regular basis throughout the day. The demands of the workforce appeared almost insatiable to the servers as queues of hungry men formed. The men were bussed from their place of work and did not have long to linger over their meals. The situation was more difficult for the few women working on site. At least the males did not have to rely solely on the toilets back at the camp.

The camp shop, selling from clothes to confectionery.

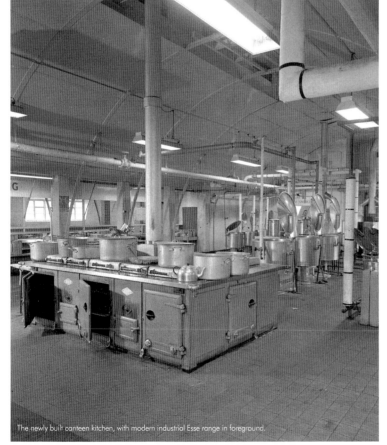

The newly built canteen kitchen, with modern industrial Esse range in foreground.

A typical staff single bedroom. Workmen slept in dormitories.

One of two canteens provided for the workmen. There were also two canteens for the 'white collar' workers.

Canteen staff – from left: Bill Henderson; Marlow Sinclair; gentleman unknown, believed to be from Wick; and Hugh Macleod. *(reproduced by kind permission of Alistair Fraser).*

Workers streaming out of the gates to...

...the buses waiting to take them back to Boston Camp.

As time progressed a noticeable difference grew between the management and the workforce. The workforce served themselves and sat at long wooden benches for their meals whilst senior staff enjoyed waitress service and sat at individual seats around cloth-covered tables.

As the workforce increased it has been suggested that a 'Wild West, frontier town atmosphere developed in the camp.' Certainly there was the odd spot of trouble and the camp stopped selling spirits and became beer only early on. But the men who came into the camp did so to earn money (the pay was well above average and overtime readily available) and the atmosphere was more sociable than wild – although Whatlings' request for a seven-day licence at the camp was still turned down. Draughts, darts, bingo (then called Lotto or Housey-Housey) and the odd game of cards passed the evening. And there was a picture show every night except Sunday when the cinema hall metamorphosed to a place of worship as a priest held evening mass (other religions were catered for elsewhere). The John O'Groat Journal faithfully reported attendances well up at local Highland games and the young Alistair Fraser, whose mother had a job as a cook in the camp, even found himself earning a glorious pound for working every weekend in the bar serving drinks.

The camp appeared to have everything; a barber, shops, a post office, a medical facility. Later, there was some grumbling about the meals and about the oldness of the films but, on the whole, it was a high time.

The first intake of apprentices: back row from left: James Mackay, Jim Thompson, John (Jock) Mackay, John Clark, Donnie Gunn – middle row: Peter (Patty) Malcolm, James (Jim) Macdonald, apprentice instructor Willie Sutherland, David Mackay, Hugh Stewart – front row: David Bremner, David Morgan.

The autumn of that year saw the first intake of apprentices. Apprentice training and the instruction of individuals was something that Dounreay was to become rightly esteemed for. Eleven young men in the fall of '55 – ten from Caithness and one from Sutherland – were taken in hand by Caithness born William Sutherland and, together, they set about establishing the training centre in a building originally constructed as part of the wartime aerodrome.

The workers, of course, found their way into Thurso and even Wick. Buses ran regularly to those towns. In early April of 1956 Thurso Town Hall ran an exhibition featuring working models and demonstrations of a nuclear plant though most of the workforce probably skipped that in favour of less sedate activities – although Thurso Library was to later complain that it did not receive its fair share of books as Dounreay was being given preference; surely suggesting some less active pastimes were indulged in.

Although the number of arrests for drunkenness and behaving in a disorderly fashion increased, overall there was little trouble in the town.

Two thoughtless painters were sent to prison for attempting to steal a car in Wick in order to return to the camp late at night and the increased car accident rate was reflected in the fact that car insurance rose in the county from being very cheap to being very dear.

The camp ceased to be a place of residence in 1960. The kitchen and dining rooms continued to be used until 1962 and after that a process of dismantling began. Today there is hardly a remnant left of the tumultuous camp and what it represented. One of the accommodation blocks was converted into a house (still to be seen) and some remain as part of the farming scenery.

The camp's part had been played.

FIRE & AMBULANCE SERVICE

Kenny Porteous.

Kenny Porteous comes from outside Caithness – from Ayrshire, in fact. After a successful career learning his trade as a fire fighter within the Imperial Chemical Industries' complex in Ardeer, Kenny joined the Dounreay Fire Brigade Service in 1981.

There had been such a service from the earliest days of Dounreay. In the beginning it was manned by volunteers from the Transport Section and much of what they were up against were domestic fires that were, more often than not, located in the camp.

As the complex developed the nature of the emergencies changed. Many of these were fires caused by the spillage of hot sodium or conflagrations of the ever-volatile NaK. These fires were fiercer and harder to deal with. In the late fifties a full time professional brigade was brought into being to tackle these new threats. It quickly developed experience with liquid metal fires and added new responsibilities when HMS Vulcan started and the brigade was then called upon to provide it with emergency cover as well (an arrangement that still runs to this day). In addition the brigade has the responsibility of providing fire cover for the airfield.

Thus, since its humble beginnings, the brigade has become ever more professional and has developed to where it can proudly boast to being amongst the most advanced in the country. It has a range of state-of-the-art equipment available including radiation monitors, radiation contamination meters, decontamination gear and thermal imaging cameras. Indeed, some of this technology it has been instrumental in developing and pioneering itself – like the new protective suits its fire fighters wear and the 'graphex' powder extinguishers they use on liquid metal fires. The very nature and location of Dounreay demands these highest of standards. Fire drill is mandatory for all members of staff. Any major incident occurring has to be contained by Dounreay's own resources for a period of up to two hours. This is unlike further south where, because of their closer proximity to regular fire brigades, site fire fighters can rely on outside help within about ten minutes of an incident starting. The brigade also owns two graphex tenders – the only ones of their kind in the world.

Brigade members attending a call out at PFR.

Each year the brigade attends between fifteen to twenty fires. Fortunately these are mostly minor in character. They also respond to over 80 ambulance calls – helping to deal with anything from cut fingers to heart attacks – and they answer around fifty special calls that can be anything from rescue to pumping operations (the Dounreay brigade are all trained ambulance technicians). And, importantly, the fire fighters have received training in the highly specialised techniques concerned in handling radiation-contaminated patients.

With a permanently manned control room, the brigade has fire fighters available at all times for all emergencies.

Chapter Six
Building the Dream

By March the 29th of 1955, Whatlings Ltd., the building and civil engineering contractors from Glasgow, had 250 men on site.

Whilst Alexander Hall and Company started building Swedish type timber houses in Thurso (April 1955) to accommodate the coming intake of workers, Whatlings and the other contractors involved set up their headquarters in the old airport control tower along with the supervising men from the Authority.

The building project itself was a truly major one, comparable to some of the greatest engineering feats of Victorian Britain. In short time a building for the main experimental fast breeder reactor had to be constructed along with its concomitant electricity generating plant and associated fuel manufacturing and reprocessing facilities; further, it had been decided that a materials test reactor with its own supporting services would also be sited at Dounreay in order to study the reaction of various substances when irradiated. In addition there were a series of laboratories required including one to study aspects of criticality; and as well as this there would be research facilities and a chemical plant for fuel reprocessing. This was on top of the administration offices, the canteen, the medical appurtenances, the police lodge, engineering workshop, the fire station and the many and various stores.

An early stage in the construction of a building.

Initially the whole 134-acre site had to be drained and the topsoil removed – drilled and blasted where necessary to lay drainage. Then trenches were dug for the services – water, waste and electrical supplies. A pipeline was laid all seven miles to Loch Shurrery to bring down the necessary fresh water. Perhaps one of the most difficult of the early undertakings however was the building of the fast reactor pump house and its associated appendages which had to cope with taking up to 50 million gallons per day from the sea for the purpose of condensing the steam generated by the reactor.

This building was sited on the rocks of the foreshore and was not that difficult to construct in itself (it was a rectangle 80 feet by 60) but a one hundred and fifty foot long channel had to be blasted through the rock to ensure the seaward end of the piping was always under at least twenty feet of water even at low tide. This meant excavating to a depth of ninety feet to accommodate the channel.

It was an arduous task for the divers concerned (twenty minutes at a time only) in laying the undersea charges and clearing the sea floor. There was an almost continuous swell on the Pentland Firth to contend with; even the land based workers, in their rubber boots, oilskins and (sometimes) helmets, found themselves frequently up to their armpits in water as the

sea swirled viciously around them. Often they were bruised and battered against the very rocks they were struggling to break up. One man had the task of standing high on the rocks to warn of any particularly large wave threatening to break. Appropriately he was named the 'wave man.' Because of the tides, work was limited to two three-hour spells a day – some of these spells were at night when the area was floodlit. Each time when finished the kit had to be lifted away as the sea returned and then brought out again as the water receded. At the worst times equipment was smashed and tools had to be sacrificed to the rage of Neptune.

The drilling for the blasting took six months – including boring through three reefs – until, eventually, one morning at 5 am (the appropriate time for the tides) all charges were let off and a long channel, some 16 feet deep, magically opened up leading down and into the sea. The pump house itself progressed slowly. The foundations had to be heavily reinforced.

The sea water pump house takes shape.

When all the excavation had been accomplished and the shuttering in place, concrete was poured in a continuous process.

Transporters came in a constant stream to feed the hungry hoppers and then monorail trucks took the concrete to the next pour – all to ensure the concrete already laid did not dry off between decantings. Small mixers together with hand barrows were used to feed the awkward areas. The whole, some 240 cubic yards of concrete, was poured in a little over 18 hours.

Although constructing the pump house was the most strenuous civil engineering project on site, perhaps the most complex, next to the reactor itself, was the construction of the plants within what was to be known as the chemical group. This was rendered difficult because of the web of underground ducting required. A most intricate grid plan for hot and cold water pipes, gas pipes, electrical cable, compressed air and vacuum pipes had to be adhered to. The high-active liquor store, within the chemical group, required that 18,000 cubic yards of rock be removed – the largest single excavation on site – prior to its construction. The storage cells here were dug well below ground level to protect and shield against any radioactive hazard. The base was lined with special concrete and the walls were clad with clay bricks that, in turn, were painted with bitumen to prevent the ingress of ground water.

To simplify these operations a brick manufacturing plant was set up off site, adjacent to the Boston camp, to reduce the overall cost of purchasing and transporting so many bricks over such a distance. The bricks were simply

Buildings in the Chemical Group, now known as the Fuel Cycle Area.

made from sand and cement, the mixture being pressed into moulds on a rotating table and as the moulds turned the bricks popped up and were then stacked to dry. This was one of the few manual tasks that saw women at work on the site. Back in Thurso, an Aberdonian company (George Bruce & Co. Ltd.) had set up a pre-cast concrete business to cope with Dounreay's demand.

Aerial view showing the DMTR foundation ring, lower left. The original runway layout is also clearly visible.

Whilst all this was going on, on the far side of the site, the east side nearest to Thurso and near the shore, the Dounreay materials test reactor (DMTR) was rising. Its construction was started in June, one month prior to Major General S. W. Joslin (ex-Commander-in-Chief of the Royal Electrical and Mechanical Engineers) arriving to take charge as the first works

manager (Joslin kept up the open policy by presenting lectures in Thurso both on atomic energy and on the specifics of what was happening). The foundations for the DMTR were in themselves a notable feat of construction. They measured 84 feet in diameter and had walls seven and a half feet thick. Some 1200 cubic yards of concrete along with 55 tons of steel reinforcement were used in their construction alone. The actual building started to rise early in 1956 and it was to reach the seventh tier, its final one, swiftly. It stood 'like an upturned dustbin' as someone said gazing at the 70 feet high building which also rejoiced in the same girth. All the steel plating around it was hermetically sealed and the 590 tons of steel had required over 10,000 feet of welding to do so.

The concrete base was designed to hold the reactor plus the twelve-foot high biological shield that would surround it. The shield consisted of an aluminium tank lined with graphite and lead and enclosed by five feet of concrete. The whole building was to be kept under a negative pressure to ensure only leakage inward could occur. Three airlocks were fitted; one for the people, the second for vehicles and the third was for emergencies.

In the Chemical Group buildings special provisions were made for the ventilation system to extract fumes through underground ducts to the ventilation stack after passing them through filters to remove any airborne radioactivity. Eventually all processing buildings would be so linked.

Pipes were also laid underground to carry liquor to the high active liquor store; the waste stored here was to be held in stainless steel vats within concrete tanks dug in well below ground level. It was designed to contain the waste until such times as it could be processed and disposed of. It was always anticipated however to discharge low-grade effluent to the sea. Earlier the original farmhouse had been converted to a laboratory and from there a radioactive tracer had been employed to feed through a

Workers in the tunnel endured damp and claustrophobic conditions.

temporary pipeline to the sea – this using water from a local stream as the carrier. Prosaically, this was termed 'Operation Squirt.' These discharges were monitored over all seasons and conditions. Samples of sand, seaweed, small rocks, and soil were taken as well as plants, leaves and flowers from along the coastline to define the spread of the tracer. A seiner fishing boat, the Primula, was kitted out with the necessary sampling equipment and was used to survey the seabed. These operations determined the optimum position for the discharge point and also established the basis for future monitoring of this nature.

Given this, work went ahead on the main waste shaft that would protect the low-level liquid waste pipeline from the force of the sea before it rose under the water some 2000 feet offshore. Many of the experienced workforce on the drilling and tunnelling were Irish having been recruited from similar work involved in Scotland's hydro-electric installations. Initially a bore was driven 200 feet down and from there the tunnel was hacked out – inches at a time and at every step of the way the rock had to be blown. Arduous work in damp and dangerous conditions and it went on round-the-clock, the darkness of the tunnel being pierced by the men's helmet lights and the few bulbs that they had managed to string in place. Water had to be pumped out at the rate of 20,000 gallons an hour and, later, the fissures through which it seeped were sealed by cement under pressure. After each controlled explosion a dump truck was filled with the debris. An adit some 213 feet deep had been driven at an angle of 1 in 3 down to join with the tunnel. Once this was done, life became somewhat easier and the work progressed more speedily. Empty trucks ran down the two-foot wide rail-track laid in the tunnel and were then filled with the debris from the rock face and hauled up the shaft.

DMTR under construction.

T.G.

TG Williams, shown right, with Major-General Joslin.

With the decommissioning of Dounreay currently scheduled to be complete by 2032, one should spare a thought for the construction pioneers of the fifties who built the majority of the 180 facilities within a five year period. It was an immense task, made that bit more difficult by the complete lack of site services and infrastructure at the start, and the ever increasing number of contractors, all with their individual priorities and demands. It called for firmness, tact and a tough mentality allied to first-class organising skills on the person charged with the day-to-day construction management of the site.

That person was Thomas George Williams, or, as he was generally known, "TG". A native of Wales, he had a very distinguished academic career having gained a first class BSc degree in mining engineering (1928) and a PhD in geology (1932), both from Cardiff University. He was also a member of the Institute of Structural Engineers, and in 1965 was appointed an OBE.

It is not recorded what "TG" thought of the barren, windswept, former airfield that confronted him, and on which he was charged to build the fast reactor which lay at the heart of the government's energy policy. Whatever thoughts he harboured, he didn't flinch from the task, and in a very short time the place started to take form.

Through a network of engineers, surveyors and clerks of work, he was responsible for ensuring that all the works were carried out according to the architects' drawings and the various specifications. There would be times when all this information didn't match up, a situation not helped by the fact that all drawings and specifications were prepared in Risley.

This would lead to tensions between the client and the contractors. On "TG's" shoulders rested the responsibility of resolving these differences. That so much complicated construction works – some never previously attempted – were achieved in such a relatively short time is testimony to his drive and vigour, and management skills.

In the history of the Dounreay nuclear site, a number of its employees have left an indelible mark. Thomas George Williams rightfully belongs to that group.

Ultimately the pipe-work for waste was laid along the adit, through the tunnel, and into a diffusing chamber from whence the contents were dispersed to the sea via vertical risers.

It was at this time that the buildings of Dounreay began to inherit their curious nomenclature. The manner in which they are named, D1100, D1200, D1300, etc., is a legacy of their construction. Instead of the UKAEA instructing the contractor to proceed with the complete construction of a particular facility, the work was ordered in logical segments against a four-digit design/cost code preceded by the letter 'D' as standing for Dounreay. This was part of the UKAEA's cost control procedures. Risley, the headquarters of the northern division that embraced Dounreay, issued instructions via an engineer's order (succinctly abbreviated to an 'EO'). The EO, as well as detailing the work to be carried out, also included the estimated cost of the work – although this part of the information was kept from the contractor. When the main administration building

was started an EO was issued to Whatlings, the main building and civil engineering contractor, showing a design/cost code of 1300 and asking of them to proceed with the necessary foundation excavations as detailed in the architectural drawing. The next EO for the subsequent stage would be numbered D1300/1 and so on and this sequential issue of EOs would continue through to completion. From the issue of the second EO, each one would contain the accumulated cost of the works. Thus, at any given time, the financial department would have a readily available indication of the costs and know whether or not the budget was being adhered to.

By the time each facility was completed their individual design/cost code would have been freely used and, whether by accident or intention, the designations stuck and they became part of Dounreay folklore.

The most famous was D1100 – DFR.

POLICE

One (police)man PC416 Vick Ford – and his dog.

The site police are a separate division from Security but, of course, are closely linked. In fact the site police, the Civil Nuclear Constabulary, are an independent body from the UKAEA. The Energy Act of 2004 split them asunder and they are now under their own police authority. The roots of this reform lie in the horror of the terrorist attack on America of September 11th 2001. Although the role of the site Constabulary has not altered since – it is still to protect the nuclear material and play their part in keeping the people of Dounreay secure – Inspector Linda Smith has seen more innovations recently than since she joined in 1977 (becoming only the third lady to enlist).

Inspector Linda Smith.

Although female influence has now spread everywhere in the force (and that is a massive change in itself) the biggest transformation Linda has noticed is a change in the perception of the role of the police. In the early days the police function lay largely in ensuring nothing unauthorised got out of Dounreay; today, it is equally, if not more so, to ensure nothing or no one gets in that is unauthorised. Linda came straight from the Northern Constabulary having patrolled Wick for over eight years. Always keen on the police as a career she had the singular privilege of enrolling at 15-and-a-half despite being half-an-inch under height. The recruiting officer opined that she would grow but, ladylike, she has obstinately refused to do so.

She trained down in Harwell for a month after joining the UKAEA Police and, as with all recruits, she received special firearms tuition. Most of the other officers were older and had come from the armed forces. Since then the force has grown in number considerably. On her drive from Wick every day to work Linda indulges in her hobby of spotting and noting wildlife.

The abiding image of Dounreay.

Chapter Seven
The Dome

D1100 will be forever associated with Dounreay and perceived as the symbol of the establishment.

It is the dome; the vast globe that dominates in dramatic silhouette the flat and empty landscape of the far west of Caithness; a feature that has been the subject of countless pictures, film shots and television scenes. A lady who has worked at Dounreay for years admits she still thrills when she sees the dome looming up as she approaches. It has come to stand for so much and mean so much to so many.

And, more strictly, the dome is actually a globe or a sphere. Its design was intended to minimise the spread of radioactivity in the event of an accidental release.

Work on the foundations of the dome had begun almost right away in 1955. Concrete was laid ten feet deep for the base. The main contractors involved were both from the central belt town of Motherwell. Alexander Findlay and Company was established in the late 1890's and was to supply much of the structural steelwork. They delivered over 5,000 tons of girders, stanchions, columns and beams before they were finished including all the maze of girders around the dome.

The Motherwell Bridge Company was the major firm involved however. They had been established in 1898 on the strength of £21,000 capital and an overdraft of £5,000. The company fortunes had more than justified the faith of those crusty Victorian gentlemen who had agreed to back it on that far distant Saturday morning. It had acquired an enviable worldwide reputation in the working of iron and steel and its endeavours were to be viewed from Liverpool through the Middle East via Bombay to Zimbabwe – not neglecting Glasgow Central Station and the bridge there known ever after as the 'Hielan' Man's Umbrella.' (This because the slick Glaswegian liked to jest that Highlanders were mean and would, during rain, prefer to cluster under the large bridge that crossed Argyll Street rather than invest a penny on a 'brolly').

The Motherwell Bridge Company established its headquarters and major workshop in one of the hangers on the aerodrome. They also brought in their own diesel generators to ensure that the fickleness of the electrical power supply in Caithness did not hold them back; in any event, the local power supply would have been unequal to the demands the heavy welding put upon it. The task facing the company was huge. New techniques in engineering technology and in welding would be required. The standards set would necessarily be the most exacting. And, added to this, there was a tight time schedule to be adhered to.

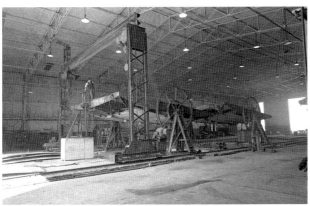

A giant press moulding the plates to an exact shape so that collectively the plates created a perfect sphere.

The company was not entirely starting on a fresh page, however. Its American associate, the Chicago Bridge Company, had already built a 225-foot sphere to house the reactor of one of the U.S.A.'s first nuclear submarines, the Sea Wolf. Importantly, the company knew the metallurgy involved together with the accompanying technology. Despite this start, it was still a novel and challenging venture.

The intent to contain any radiation determined the standards of construction. The steel decided upon was a type known as 'Coltuf.' This was selected because, whilst adding no extra strength, it did not become brittle at ultra low temperatures. This was not a safeguard against the Caithness weather but a practical step as, should radiation ever leak out, exposure to such was believed to have the same effect as low temperatures.

Designed to have an internal pressure slightly lower than outside to keep any escaping gases in, each weld in the dome's accumulative two miles of welding across the 1.5 acres of metal plating had to be perfect. Any flaw in a weld could expand itself and open out, possibly leading to a failure of containment and, hence, cause the complete shutdown of the plant. Thus all the vital welding had to be x-rayed on site. The welders were amongst the best in the country (they all had to possess Lloyds' qualification) and they often had to labour high up on the sphere from scaffolding or inside in enclosed claustrophobic spaces. Because they frequently had to weld over zinc, the Motherwell Bridge Company insisted they drank plenty of milk everyday to offset the effects of the fumes.

The exacting time schedule meant that the sphere's panels had to be prefabricated in one of the specially adapted hangers on site although most of the work was still carried out in the steel town of Motherwell itself. Since the base of the sphere had to allow for the ingress of over 330 pipes and cables all the nozzles and entry points were welded in Motherwell. This led to a transportation problem when the largest piece of the lower half of the sphere had to be brought up from that town. It was sent by sea to Scrabster and, there being no cranes large enough to off-load it, it had to be ported on deck and unloaded at low tide when the deck was at the same level as the low-loader which had been brought in to take it on the last leg of its journey to site. At Dounreay, as at Scrabster, skids were used; this time to ease it off the vehicle and manoeuvre it to its resting spot.

By the end of 1955 the lower half of the sphere was in place.

Wisely, remembering the previous winter, the tent makers, Thomas Black of Greenock, were called in to provide a huge umbrella for the half-completed sphere. Again the scale was massive. Black's used over 1,100 yards of 36-inch wide, 18 ounce unboiled flax to stitch together a covering to permit the work to continue unabated underneath even under extreme weather conditions. Indeed, the long hours involved and the fact that the Sabbath was being worked on drew comment. Caithness County Council objected, as did the Lord's Day Observance Society and the Caithness Employers' Federation. The amount of work on offer simply meant that other employers could not compete with the earnings of the Dounreay workers and they complained they were starved of manpower. In the end nothing came of these protests; Councillor George Gunn made the point that in war men are in action all the time and the need to construct Dounreay swiftly was akin to economic war.

Nevertheless the Lord's Day Observance Society surely had a point when it questioned the efficiency of men working up to 70 hours per week.

The airlock giving access into the sphere.

It was early April in that year of 1957 when the sphere – now beginning to look like a sphere – was ready for the heart of the reactor to be sited in it. The stainless steel vessel into which the reactor had to be lowered was dubbed the 'pot.' It took 18 months to construct to the extremely tight tolerances necessary to ensure it was completely leak proof. The welding was inspected painstakingly inch by inch with over 4,000 x-ray films being taken. It left the premises of John Thompson Water Tube Boilers Ltd. in Dudley in Worcestershire some thirteen days before it made its appearance in Caithness. The 105-foot long Pickford's trailer, with a three-man crew (one steering the independent back wheels), crawled along the roads with a police escort at little over five miles per hour. The total load weighed around 90 tons with the pot being 13 feet 9 inches high and with a 12 foot

SAFE AND SOUND

Perhaps a more obviously essential department than Archives, particularly these troubled days, is the Security section. Led by Glasgow born Malcolm Clark, this division has the task of advising management on security issues and also on the security implications of various matters. This involves everything from deciding on the optimum placement of security cameras to the elaborate procedures required for V.I.P. visits. Malcolm came from the Royal Air Force into Aldermaston (the Ministry of Defence Atomic Weapons Establishment) where he spent two happy years dealing with the earnest but irritating peace campaigners. When he and his wife came to Caithness they loved it from the start even although the temperature was minus three and snow was on the ground on the first day they arrived.

Unlike Malcolm, security administrator Elspeth Anderson is Caithness born and bred, coming from Mey originally. She has the day-to-day task of the supervising and the controlling, checking and vetting of the over 2,000 individuals who enter the site each twenty-four hours either as members of staff, contractors or as site visitors of one sort or another (over 3,000 individuals have passes). She remembers when typewriter ribbons and carbon papers had to be locked away when they had been used to produce sensitive information. Now computers have taken over, much easier to produce memoranda and letters on but causing an even greater security challenge. Indeed security is, today, an integral part of the business process and electronic devices such as computers, digital cameras and cellular mobile phones make protection of data ever more complex.

Malcolm Clark.

Elspeth Anderson.

9 inch girth. Inevitably it became stuck on the famous Berriedale Braes and also at the single-track bridge at Forss. Sleepers had to be used to raise the load above the parapets but, cheered by the people who had come out to see it pass, it eventually reached its destination and its destiny when it was lowered through the top of the dome into its pride of place in the middle of the sphere.

In early May the capping-piece for the dome was in place and on the 22nd of May 1957, the dome began its final pressure and vacuum tests – a series that took four days. It passed with flying colours.

The dome was finished, at least on the outside. At 135 feet high, its over 1500 tons of steel dominated the site. The steel varied from one and an eighth to one and three quarter inches thick and, inside, some 7,000 tons of concrete lined the lower half. Specially designed cigarette lighters in the shape of the dome were handed out to the Motherwell Bridge staff involved. Thurso's local paper, the Caithness Courier, revealed the dome was to be painted white and some 500 gallons of paint would be needed.

Now the scientists could come in.

Danny Doohan.

GETTING PAID

Danny Doohan (now retired) is another who has been ever active upon Dounreay's behalf. Danny was with the UKAEA since he left school. Initially he worked in the recruitment department when he joined in 1958 at Risley. Possibly as a reward for expressing dissatisfaction at the way some aspects of the business was then being run, he was asked whether he would like to transfer to Dounreay. He was flown up to look at the site and deposited in Ormlie Lodge for an overnight stay – where he found a party in full swing. Perhaps that's what swayed him but he agreed to join immediately (both Dounreay and the party). Although he came up into Stores, he was one of the first to train on the new wonder of computers that were then being introduced and he moved into Wages and Salaries. He can remember having to drive down to Leeds overnight to use computers there when the ever-reliable ones at Dounreay had broken down again. Then he had to drive back the next day (missing most of his sleep) with the outputs – despite this he spent ten happy years in computer programming.

Danny was promoted down south to Risley for a period but he was glad to return and move into the contracts department afterwards – taking it over, in fact. Decommissioning was being talked about then and the policy was towards privatisation. Much of the work had to be placed out to contract to satisfy the new privatisation procedures and this involved dealing with suppliers, the preparing of tenders and the adjudging of quotations.

Building the Dream

Whilst the Dounreay site is made up of some one hundred and eighty buildings, it is the sphere, designed by Frank Brocklesby, which is its most universally recognisable feature. The following sequence, captured by the Dounreay photographic section, shows the sphere taking form, as it reached up into the northern sky, heralding the nuclear age to Caithness.

April 1955 – a month after the site was opened up, and construction of the sphere's foundations has commenced...

...with a raft of concrete being laid to support the sphere and the reactor vault. But initially, this foundation has another important role...

A steel structure is fixed dead centre, from which a web of steel guy-ropes hold each steel plate in place, prior to them being welded.

Early August 1955, and already the upper base of the sphere is well advanced. This picture captures graphically the role of the guy ropes.

No, this man is not using a mobile phone! He is shielding his eyes as welders butt the steel plates together.

By the end of August 1955, the upper base of the sphere is complete, and...

...within another month, the sphere is almost at its halfway point.

November 1955, and the halfway point has been reached, including the fixing of the mid-point walkway. Note the workman standing in the 'hole'. This hole is where the airlock chamber would be later installed.

Spring 1956, and work has commenced on the structure that will house the all-important fast reactor, and...

...by June, the steelwork is complete, and concreting the reactor vault roof is in full swing.

One month later, looking somewhat forlorn in its isolation, construction of the sphere has reached three-quarter point.

October 1956. The sphere continues its upward spiral, and a start has been made on the construction of its ancillary buildings.

March 1957, and the sphere is all but complete, except for the final capping piece. This has been left off to allow large pieces of equipment to be inserted through this opening, including the reactor vessel, that meantime...

...was experiencing difficulty negotiating Forss bridge! By the use of sleepers, the carriageway is raised sufficiently to allow the load through. Morris Wyatt, head of engineering, and T G Williams, the resident engineer, do not look too concerned!

The reactor vessel, the component central to the Government's energy policy, is now safely in storage at Dounreay. All that remains to be done is to fit it into the sphere.

April 1957, and this vital task commences. Gradually the vessel commences its lift. To clear the uppermost part of the sphere, the vessel requires to be raised to a height of over 150ft. The Lowry-like people milling around seem almost oblivious to this piece of history in the making. Note the precarious positions used by a number of people to get a grandstand view.

The vessel is now directly above the opening. The crane driver now has the tricky job of guiding it through. "I wonder what way the wind is blowing", he might be thinking to himself!

It's safely through, without a scratch. Now, who can that be peering through the opening?

Some kind of walkie-talkie system must have been used to keep in contact with the crane-driver as he gradually lowers, blindly, the vessel...

August 1957. WIth the sphere capping-piece in place, gradually the cranes that had dominated the skyline for the past two years are being dismantled. The reactor's ancillary building, the heat-exchanger, the diesel generator house, and the admin building, are all very advanced.

...into the reactor vault. And so, in April 1957, a seminal moment in fast reactor history is achieved.

May 1958, construction is complete, the cranes and the scaffolding have all gone. Meanwhile, inside the sphere there is great activity as miles of cabling and pipework are being installed and linked up to a bewildering range of plant and equipment. All day and throughout the night, the work contines to ensure the dream would work. But that's another story...

Chapter Eight
Open Day

Despite the early days of 1957 reminding the anxious Dounreay staff of the beginnings of '55 as the snows returned with blizzard force, Dounreay was running to schedule. The final cost was in the region of £15 million and some 2,300 persons were currently being employed on the project of which at least half were local people.

The feeling of confidence within the UKAEA extended to holding an open day to show off the establishment. It was a splendid day in that far off month of May and one of those days that people who were there remember well. An exhibition attempting to explain the technology and what Dounreay was about was held in Thurso Town Hall simultaneously with a similar one in the Highland capital of Inverness – concurrent with open day. The day previous to open day had been reserved for the press. Journalists had come from all over. There were Dutch, Germans, Belgians, Americans, Swedish, Russians, Danish, Japanese and others. Groups of reporters were escorted round ten at a time to marvel at the miracle accomplished in the creation of Dounreay. At the end of a long day, Sir Christopher Hinton gave them an audience backed with leading members from Dounreay's staff including the formidable Major-General Joslin.

Hinton again came over well. He dealt with the issue of safety by stating that the very design of the Dome would cope with what he foresaw as the most serious possible of accidents, ranging from a liquid metal fire to a core meltdown.

Hinton also covered something of the economics of the emerging nuclear industry but it was the Major-General who made it clear that Dounreay was not about generating income. It was to be a research establishment, pure and simple. Even the recent announcement that the Royal Navy was to build a reactor (to test the engines of its nuclear submarines) at its base next door to Dounreay (HMS Vulcan) was dealt with. Hinton explained that whilst the UKAEA was responsible for the civil work at HMS Vulcan's

reactor that was as far as it went. He did however also reveal an intention that experimental work related to powering surface ships with nuclear reactors would be carried out using the Dounreay materials test reactor. The following day, as the general public descended on the site Hinton, perhaps wisely, cleared off to the Orkneys for a holiday with his wife.

For many, this was their first glimpse of the future.

The scale of the turnout surprised the UKAEA. Before the opening hour of 10 am there were long queues and a fleet of buses kept arriving with even more. Perhaps not from as far-flung locations as the press they nevertheless came from all over the Highlands and, indeed, from all over Scotland; and there were even interested parties from far off darkest England. Most were in the uniform of the time – cloth cap and trench coat for the men and flower bonnet and camel coat for the ladies. Well over 7,000 arrived. They came out of an earnest desire to learn the marvels that science was revealing and they listened carefully to what the sometimes harassed white-coated

DINING OUT

The Fuel Cycle Area canteen.

Dounreay has always empathised with the requirements of its employees – particularly with those with special needs – and one aspect of this is the concern it takes over its all-important catering arrangements. Possibly the early criticisms that catering received in the days of the camp helped to ensure a higher standard thereafter; with Dounreay being isolated as it is there is no opportunity to pop out to a nearby café or restaurant for a quick snack or lunch.

The main restaurant operated during the day and a smaller restaurant, adjacent to it, was known as the shift-canteen. This operated around the clock to deal with the demands of shift-workers because in the early days there were no tea-bars. There was also a waitress service area that was used, almost exclusively, by management and senior staff. In addition there was a shop, separated from the restaurants, where food could be purchased. The director had a personal dining room but this was generally reserved for use only on those occasions when visitors were being entertained.

Initially UKAEA employees staffed the canteen; the first manager was Victor Barrington who was also a qualified football referee. Gradually a series of local tea-bars spread throughout the site and canteen staff had the task of delivering sandwiches, filled rolls, pies and sausage rolls to these on a daily basis. Eventually vending machines took over much of this service. The main management buildings (D1300 and D8538) had a trolley service that went round them as well – feeding the hungry with tea and coffee along with biscuits and other snacks.

One of the main changes was when D1201 was decommissioned and the area became a changing room and a canteen. This allowed the shift-canteen to be used in a more general way and when Fuel Services were established the building that housed the library became their headquarters. The waitress service dining room was then closed and converted to use as the library.

In the '90s increasing use was being made of vending machines whilst the shop was closed and its range of goods merged with those available in the canteen. In 1994 the outsourcing of specialised activities was in full swing and catering came under the auspices of Procord (later taken on by Johnson Controls). The only change since is that Johnson Controls, who are responsible for many aspects of the site, have sub-contracted catering to Eurest who specialise in large scale catering. Even in these days when most individuals snack on sandwiches or have merely a bowl of soup at lunch, Eurest, with their 26 full-time operators, still provide up to 500 meals a day in the main restaurant on top of provisioning all the tea bars and sandwich stores throughout the site.

The intricacies of modern science being explained to the visitors.

technicians were telling them as they trudged round the laboratories, fuel fabrication plants, reprocessing facilities, and waste stores. They were allowed to try their hand at manipulating the robot arms behind the thick glass walls of glove boxes (Hinton had told the press that each box cost about £2,400) that, ultimately, would be used to handle radioactive material.

Alistair Fraser, by then a youth all of fifteen, was given the privilege of being taken to the dome and up onto the mid-point walkway. From there he climbed to the top by clambering up ladders and over scaffolding that was tied to the outer skin by temporary lugs. When he finally reached the top a team of workers were smoothing the ring of weld that united the final capping piece with the sphere. Apart from feeling like the great statue that overlooks Rio de Janeiro his abiding memory is of how flat the top was and what a great view he got of all that was going on down below.

The star attraction was indeed the dome and what lay hidden within its walls. The Saltire flew from its top. A brave and confident symbol of the new technology housed within. Explanations were given as to the principles of fast reactors and the theory behind them but the statistic that everyone there remembers best was that it, the dome, cost almost £6 million – this in a time when the average wage was less than £10 per week.

It was time for a cup of tea and this too Dounreay provided to its guests. In the words of one reporter commenting on the humour of the crowd, 'It wasn't quite a fairground atmosphere, but it was so near.'

If they did not know before, the local Caithness people certainly knew after that day what a huge undertaking was on their doorstep.

Again the UKAEA had demonstrated its good will and desire to be a good neighbour and be as open as possible.

It was around this time that James Malcolm entered service at Dounreay. His story is typical of many and demonstrates the opportunities the Authority was providing. Unemployed at seventeen, James faced moving south or a life in and out of the Labour Exchange taking what jobs he could get. Dounreay took him on because he missed having to do National Service (by only one important month). UKAEA was organised into six main divisions at that time. The Reactor division ran the reactors, Engineering provided a comprehensive engineering and design facility, Metallurgical were responsible for handling the fuel elements and research on new materials, Chemistry were accountable for the recovery of radioactive materials and the control of waste and then there was the Administration division. Finally there was the all-important Health and Safety division, which had (and whose modern equivalent has) a total responsibility on all matters that could threaten health – from checking on individuals to monitoring of the environment. James joined this division as a safety attendant (earning less than £3 per week). His first work was ensuring gas bottles were filled and checking that respirators were working properly. He hated it and was going to leave after a week. The culture of formality and collar and ties was new to him.

However, he stuck it out for 47 years and readily agrees that it provided him and his family with a living and a security that otherwise they could not have enjoyed. And he did get to love it in the end.

Fifteen days after open day, the UKAEA took formal possession of the Dounreay fast reactor (DFR) from the Motherwell Bridge Company.

James Malcolm on his retiral, pictured with his wife.

THE DOUNREAY LOCAL LIAISON COMMITTEE

The Dounreay Local Liaison Committee was established in 1957 with the following terms of reference:-

"A local Dounreay Local Liaison Committee is to be formed, with the object of keeping local authorities and others interested in local affairs informed of the progress of the work at Dounreay and the measures being adopted to ensure the safety of the countryside. In emergency this committee would meet as frequently as necessary to decide on any steps required to safeguard local inhabitants and industries such as fishing and agriculture, and to put these measures into effect. At other times the committee will meet periodically. Meetings will be held wherever most convenient to members, but it may be desirable to hold them at Dounreay, so that those members who wish to do so can make a tour of the site and see for themselves the plans being made to ensure district safety."

Initially the Committee was comprised of members from the various adjoining local authorities along with such organisations as the Department of Agriculture and Fisheries, the North of Scotland Milk Marketing Board and various government and medical and hospital representatives as well as senior members of the UKAEA and HMS Vulcan management.

The first chairman was Dr. Robert Hurst, the Dounreay director, and this began the tradition of having the director chair the committee; a tradition that, along with the holding of the meeting at Dounreay, attracted a fair share of criticism. With the committee's secretary being a Dounreay employee as well, this meant that the committee was sometimes perceived as simply a creature of Dounreay's. However, the arrangement was largely practical as, inevitably, Dounreay would take the lead in most discussions.

The new Dounreay Stakeholder Group in session.

The average membership of the committee was twenty-five and it normally met once a year. However, some thirty years were to elapse from its inception before the press were allowed to attend and, as a further move to increase public awareness, minutes of the meeting were displayed in public libraries in Caithness, Sutherland and Orkney.

In April 2005, the Nuclear Decommissioning Authority (NDA) took over the management of all nuclear sites. They demanded a much more open and transparent forum in which to have a dialogue with the public; a forum with an independent chairman and a forum that would be advertised and held in appropriate venues to permit public attendance. As a consequence, the DLLC became redundant. Its final meeting was held in February of 2005. The first meeting of the new forum, the Dounreay Stakeholder Group, took place on March 2006 in a Thurso hotel where the local Highland councillor was elected chairman.

Chapter Nine
Criticality

The target date for criticality of the main reactor (DFR) was set for April 1958.

But it was neither the Dounreay fast reactor nor the smaller Dounreay materials test reactor that attained the honour of being the first reactor to achieve criticality on Scottish soil.

The criticality team in front of D1249. From left: Vic Parker, Eric Thornthwaite, Alan Bray, JC Smith, Gordon Hansen, Hugh Paxton, John Walford, Roy Reider, Jimmy Lyons, Bob Hack, George White. Hansen, Paxton and Reider were visiting site from the Los Alamos nuclear laboratory in the US.

The historic moment occurred at lunchtime on the 13th of August 1957. It was the much smaller and lesser-known ZETR (zero energy test reactor) that unassumingly accomplished the miracle (and miracle is the correct word). ZETR was a water-reflected solution reactor brought to Dounreay from Harwell in 1956 and located in the unglamorously termed cell 1 of building D1249. It continued to operate carrying out a variety of experiments until early 1961.

But that only added to the buzz about Dounreay as Dr. Robert Hurst, married and with three sons, took over as its first director in the spring of 1958 giving a clear sign that the main building days were over and that Dounreay was going to settle into what it was intended to be; namely a scientific establishment developing the nuclear fast breeder reactor as an energy source.

Also that spring the Caithness Courier ran a story on the problems some of the new people settled in Thurso were having. It was all rather familiarly reassuring in its everydayness. They complained of the hygiene standards at some of the butchers, they complained of the speed of traffic in Ormlie Road, they complained about the difficulty in obtaining dental treatment.

Encouraged, no doubt, by its smaller brother ZETR, the Dounreay materials test reactor was brought to criticality at 2.45 am on Saturday, May the 24th, 1958.

The DMTR, a thermal (or slow) reactor, was designed to enable various materials being considered for use in future reactors to be tested. Such materials used in the construction of reactors or as fuels or as coolants could be irradiated in the neutron flux of DMTR under controlled conditions and have their behaviour monitored. Using the DMTR various substances could receive, in a very short time, the expected irradiation dose that they would acquire over many years of normal working as part of a nuclear reactor. The knowledge gained would then be applied to the design of future reactors. Thus the importance of the DMTR.

The method of testing was simple. The materials to be tested were inserted into the DMTR in special rigs and irradiated to the required degree. Then they were removed and examined.

DMTR nearing completion.

Unlike its bigger brother, which was to use liquid metal, DMTR used heavy water as its moderator and coolant. The core consisted of 28 box sections of fuel elements (enriched uranium) and these were mounted vertically in a cylindrical aluminium tank containing the heavy water. The tank was encompassed by a graphite reflector and enclosed in steel that, in turn, was surrounded by a lead shield; then concrete walls around all further shielded the whole.

The reactor was sited directly under the heavy water plant room that housed the pump and heat exchanger units. These were designed to take the heat from the heavy water and transfer it to ordinary H_2O. No less than eight large cooling units dissipated the heat to atmosphere.

Oddly, it was not long after that, the start of criticality, that a letter appeared in the press querying the long-term future of Dounreay and asking what would replace it afterwards and at the same time Sir Christopher Hinton, now Chairman of the Central Electricity Generating Board, began questioning the cost of nuclear generated power.

The fuel element load/unload flask carrying out routine refuelling operations.

The seawater pumphouse following completion, showing the 150 foot intake channel.

If DMTR was up and running well, delay still dogged the start-up of DFR.

Earlier a much-publicised accident at Windscale, another of the UKAEA's plants, had caused a significant delay as resources were siphoned off to tackle the consequences of that. More immediate to Dounreay however, the seawater pump house had flooded and required to be shut down for several days. Seaweed had washed in and blocked the outer channel (the beginning of the never quite solved seaweed problem).

Another problem was, perhaps, more important. When attempting to free jammed control units, it had been necessary to rotate the shields above the reactor. Whenever this operation was undertaken it broke the mechanical seals (temporarily) and put sole reliance on the mercury dip seals (as designed for) but liquid metal accidentally splashed into the mercury and formed a high melting point alloy which froze and this caused a marked hold-up; adding pure mercury and removing the amalgam recovered the situation.

As much as anything though the delay was a function of the care being taken. Dry runs on loading and unloading the fuel elements were carried out before the liquid metal coolant (sodium-potassium or NaK as it was known) or the radioactive uranium fuel was charged into the system.

Still, if the Dounreay fast reactor was behind schedule, James Cross MacDonald wasn't. He became the first individual to complete a craft

James Cross MacDonald receiving his indentures from Morris Wyatt.

apprenticeship through the courses at Dounreay. At twenty-one, he was an electrician.

Eventually the problems surrounding the reactor were overcome. The core was then loaded progressively with fuel elements. As a precaution only four such elements at a time (each separately numbered and with its individual history recorded) were taken out from the fuel store in order to avoid accidental criticality. The ebb and flow of the elements were mimicked on a pegboard designed to correspond to the layout of the reactor core. When there were 227 elements in the core it was calculated that another seven would be required for criticality. However, ten were on stand-by in case needed to ensure success.

On Saturday the 13th of November 1959, at eight minutes to eleven in the morning (and a week after the Fast Reactor Design Committee had met for the last time), William Munro, who had been a farm labourer prior to Dounreay and was then a charge hand process worker, loaded the final fuel element into the reactor that pushed the reactor into criticality.

William afterwards stated he was thrilled to play a part in it and there was jubilation all round among the innumerable visitors and other interested parties that had assembled as the core produced some 18 watts of power.

This was the high point of Dounreay's existence up until that moment: the point that so many dedicated people, scientists, engineers, technicians, and all the staff had worked so conscientiously for over five hard years since the inception of the site.

Or, depending how you look at it, what humanity had worked towards for almost 2,500 hard years.

William Munro and family – back, from left, William, Brian and David Munro. Front: Jean and William Munro. Taken shortly after criticality. (Reproduced by kind permission of Brian Munro).

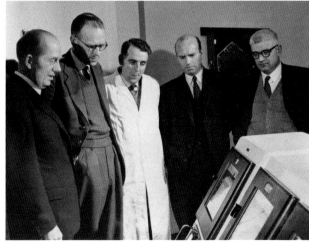

Dr Hurst, right, Dounreay director, along with senior colleagues, intently check the control desk readings, as the fast reactor starts operating for the first time – November 1959.

Chapter Ten
The Historical Background

The first person credited by history to propose that matter could not be divided endlessly was the Greek philosopher Leucippus (496 BC-5 BC). He suggested that however often you divided a substance you had to reach a point where a fundamental particle existed that could no longer be broken down into anything smaller.

Leucippus's pupil Democritus (460-370 BC) termed these particles 'atomos' meaning 'unbreakables.' Democritus considered that all matter consisted of atomos and, if there was space between them, then that space was simply an empty void.

Epicurus (341-270 BC) supported and advanced this theory. He used it to bring the gods under control. He visualised the whole universe as consisting solely of atomos and void and thus the gods themselves had to be composed of atomos and, as such, had to be subject to natural laws.

Not all that intelligent Greek thought was actually correct but it is a sad reflection that it was only a lonely few (including people like Hero of Alexandria and Giovanni Bruno) that kept atomism alive until the 17th century when men returned to such speculations and attempted to give them solid form.

One such was the Irishman Robert Boyle (1627-1691) who carried out an experiment pouring mercury into a glass tube shaped like the letter 'J.' This tube had its short leg closed and its long leg open. The mercury filled the bottom of the tube and some of the long leg but only rose partly up the short leg. It thus trapped the air there (in the short leg) and, in turn, was stopped by that air from rising further up. Boyle found that adding more mercury via the long leg squeezed the air even more, reducing the space occupied by the air in the short leg.

Boyle built up a distinctive pattern relating to the amount of air space and the volume of compressed air. He recognised that the behaviour of the air, its contraction under pressure, could be explained by Democritus's reasoning that air consisted of atomos with only space separating them.

Although there would still be arguments, from Boyle onwards the existence of 'atomos' became more and more accepted.

This was further confirmed by the work of Joseph Louis Proust of France (1754-1826) who discovered that when elements combined to form more complex substances they did so in fixed relationships – again substantiating the existence of 'atomos.' Shortly after this the English chemist John Dalton (1766-1844) corroborated Proust's work and expanded it. To account for the behaviour of materials Dalton concluded that each element was made up of atoms (we'll call them that now as Dalton named them so in tribute to Democritus) that were all entirely the same in every way and that all elements consisted of atoms entirely unique to themselves. Dalton published his findings in a book, 'The New System of Chemical Philosophy,' in 1808.

From that moment modern atomic theory – as opposed to ancient Greek – was born.

Another strand of the atomic story was a strange one. Robert Brown (1773 – 1858) was born the son of the manse in Montrose. His contribution to atomic theory came when he observed movement (later termed 'Brownian motion' in his honour) in small, microscopic particles of grains of pollen suspended in a fluid. This perplexing movement was to take a genius of the first order to work out the reason for it.

ACHILLES VERSUS TORTOISE

According to Aristotle, the early atomists were inspired by the many paradoxes suggested by Zeno (circa 495 – 430 BC). Zeno was a pupil of Parmenides (circa 515 BC) and he defended his fellow citizen's philosophical belief that reality is a single, changeless and homogeneous phenomenon (the young Socrates conversed with both Zeno and Parmenides).

In defence of this position, Zeno used arguments designed to demonstrate that the world is not as straightforward as it appears (in agreement with modern quantum mechanics). There are a number of versions of the type of reasoning he employed but one runs thus:-

The cunning tortoise challenges Achilles to a race. Achilles laughs as he knows that he can run ten times faster than the tortoise. The tortoise is willing to place a bet on his winning if only Achilles gives him a ten-yard start.

'Right,' says Achilles.
'Give me your money then,' answers the tortoise.
'But, we haven't raced yet!'
'No point: I would win,' replies the sly creature, 'and I can prove it.'
Achilles is suspicious and demands an explanation.
'You give me a ten yards start,' elucidates the tortoise, 'and you race that ten yards. Now, you run ten times faster than I, so how far will I have gone in the time it takes you to cover the first ten yards?'
'That's easy,' answers Achilles, 'You'll be – uh – let's see – ah, you'll be a yard ahead of me.'
'Good. And how far ahead of you will I be when you cover that yard?'
Again the great man considers. 'Why, you'll be a tenth of a yard ahead.'
'There you are,' triumphantly asserts the tortoise, 'No matter how much of my lead you catch up, I'll always be one tenth of the last distance ahead of you! Pay me my money.'
And, after a long thought, Achilles did so.
The Greeks knew the tortoise's reasoning was flawed and that, in practice, Achilles would have won easily but they recognised the difficulty in disproving the 'logic' of the tortoise.
One answer to the problem (and the Greeks lacked the sophisticated mathematical tools that were only developed in the 16th century and would solve it mathematically) the Greeks considered that there comes eventually a unit of distance so small that it can be no longer sub-divided and through which Achilles will rapidly pass to catch the tortoise.
Aristotle, no less, claimed that this type of argument was instrumental with the early atomists when they became convinced that there must exist incredibly small and indivisible particles of matter.

James Clerk Maxwell (1831-1879) was such a one; but he did not pick up on Brown's work. Instead this Edinburgh man grasped that the behaviour of gases was caused by the fact that the molecules and atoms of which they were comprised were in constant motion. This work illumined the puzzle of temperature. Maxwell showed that temperature was simply the measure of the average speed at which atoms were wizzing about in a body. Later, Maxwell laid the basis of modern physics with his great papers describing electro-magnetic fields in complex differential equations involving space and time.

Maxwell left the solving of Brownian motion up to a younger genius – a genius who also took up Maxwell's work on space and time.

It was in 1905 that Albert Einstein (1879-1955) put forward his thesis that Brownian motion was caused by the small grains of pollen being jiggled by the constant bombardment of the atoms and molecules of the solution they were suspended in striking them at random.

Einstein demonstrated this mathematically but it was the Frenchman Jean Baptiste Perrin (1870-1942) who displayed the experimental reality. He placed a fine powder of gum resin in a container of water. If Einstein was correct the particles would never completely settle and the dispersion of their rising and falling and the amount at any level at one time would be predictable. Conversely, was Einstein to be wrong, the particles would eventually form a solid mass in the bottom.

The particles behaved as per Einstein.

The last doubts as to the existence of atoms were resolved.

Strands tangled with strands; a lot of strands make up the background of nuclear power. As the existence of atoms was being resolved the English physicist Joseph Thomson (1856-1940) was experimenting with cathode rays – first observed by Michael Faraday. Thomson discovered the rays were charged, swinging away from a negatively charged plate and towards the positive. From earlier work by Faraday on the amount of electricity required to bring about deposition of specific quantities of metal from a solution, Thomson calculated the size of the particle making up the cathode stream. The result staggered the scientific world. The particle proved to have only the mass of 1/1837th of the smallest atom.

This was the first sub-atomic particle to be found. Thomson named it the electron and its mass is given (today) at 0.00000000000000000000000000091091 grams.

So by 1905 atoms were accepted as real entities and that sub-atomic particles also existed; and there was more.

X-rays had been discovered (by the German scientist Wilhelm Roentgen, 1845-1923) and the Frenchman Henri Becquerel (1852-1908), whilst working with X-rays had stumbled across the fact that uranium emits a radiation all by itself.

Following Becquerel, the husband and wife team of Pierre (1859-1906) and Marie Curie (1867-1934) devoted their lives to the study of these natural radiations. They found other elements that emitted rays – it was Marie who coined the term 'radioactivity.' In 1902, the Curies pronounced on the intensity of the energy they observed radioactivity releasing.

But it was the New Zealander, Ernest Rutherford (1871-1937), a hale and hearty individual, who proved that radioactive substances could emit more than one type of ray. Rutherford suggested that the atom might contain large volumes of energy and that radiation was simply a spontaneous outpouring of a little of that energy; which brings back Mr. Einstein.

The other theory that Einstein produced in 1905 was to become known as the special theory of relativity. This was to prove earth shattering – or, more accurately, universe shattering. Einstein had taken Maxwell's equations and from them proposed that light was both a particle and a waveform and that for all observers' frames of reference its speed was the same; it was time and motion that were relative.

Finally he suggested that matter (m) was simply a form of energy (e), frozen energy perhaps but energy all the same, and that thus matter related to energy and the speed of light (c) and, all importantly, matter could thus be converted back into energy.

$E = MC^2$ in fact.

The following year Rutherford carried out further significant experiments. He bombarded gold leaf with a type of radiation called alpha particles. As expected they streamed through the gold leaf – at least the vast majority. Every now and then one or two would bounce off. It was as if they were striking something quite massive. Rutherford believed they were hitting the dense heart of the atom.

From these experiments, Rutherford described the atom as having its positive charge in the incredibly tiny centre that he termed the nucleus.

BOYLE'S LAW

The experiments Boyle carried out on the reaction of gas to pressure eventually provided sufficient data for a law to be formulated.

Known as 'Boyle's Law' in his honour it states that the product of the volume and pressure of a fixed quantity of an ideal gas is constant, given constant temperature.

LAWMEN

Proust's work eventually ended in a law being recognised, the Law of Definite Proportions. This states that every chemical compound contains fixed and constant proportions (by weight) of its constituent elements. Dalton's expansion of this became known as the Law of Multiple Proportions and this states that when any two elements combine with each other to form more than one compound, the weights of one element that combine with a fixed weight of the other are in a ratio of small whole numbers.

Virtually the entire mass of the atom is in the nucleus that occupies (dependent on the element) between $1/10,000^{th}$ to $1/100,000^{th}$ of the diameter but less than one trillionth of the volume of the whole. Outside the nucleus, the remainder of the atom consists of nothing but electrons that orbit the nucleus.

In general, the larger an atom is (that is the more electrons it has and the larger the nucleus it must have) the less stable it is. This instability stems from the heart of the atom. The situation is (somewhat) analogous to the old fruit market porters at Covent Garden when they would carry baskets of fruit on top of their heads. With only one basket up, the porter could carry the load indefinitely; two, three or four – perfectly stable. Twenty could still be carried but not quite as securely and there would be rare crashes. You could not predict what load would fall or when but you knew, from the sheer volume of loads, that there would be the occasional accident.

So it was with the less stable atoms; from time to time they released a burst of radiation before settling down into a more stable state. And that radiation represented a release of energy.

In the 1930's scientists attempted to develop heavier and heavier atoms by bombarding uranium with neutrons. They found that the uranium nucleus could split under such an onslaught. Instead of simply calling this process nucleus splitting, they complicated matters and termed it nuclear fission.

It was the team of Meitner and Hahn who expanded this work in the late 30's. Lise Meitner (1878-1968) was Jewish and she eventually had to flee to Sweden – thus losing the Third Reich an extremely able scientist. The Nazis had already lost Leo Szilard (1898-1964) a Hungarian Jew who had fled to Britain and who was the first person (in 1934) to file for a patent on nuclear chain reactions. Szilard eventually worked with Fermi in Chicago on the first reactor.

Meitner's nephew, Otto Frisch (1904-1979), aided Meitner in her work. Together they formalised nuclear fission. Meitner suggested that the bombardment of uranium that Otto Hahn (1879-1968) was undertaking was effectively breaking the nucleus in half. In fact it was quickly recognised that the nucleus does not necessarily break into equal parts and nor does it always break in the same fashion.

But it does break and it does release a considerable lot of energy when it does and that led on to those first halting steps in Chicago and the nuclear reactor.

Chapter Eleven
DFR

The nuclear reactor that achieved criticality at Dounreay at the back end of 1959 was, at heart, a simple piece of apparatus once the theory of it was known.

It was a bold concept though. There were concerns at the time that uranium was in short supply (fears that later proved unfounded) and that there was a need to develop a reactor that would use it efficiently and be capable of breeding its own fuel, plutonium. Given that knowledge of such reactors was limited, the British designers had only an incomplete template to work from. Nevertheless it was decided to aim for a plant large enough to produce meaningful power in itself and also one that would be an archetype for a full-scale fast reactor power station to be built later.

Although DFR was to be much smaller than subsequent plants, it compared well with others at the time. The Obninsk plant in the USSR had been the first commercial plant to feed electricity on-line (June 1954) and it produced a 'mere' 5MW (thermal); the Arco plant in Idaho came shortly after with 3.5MW (thermal) but Calder Hall upped the stakes when it went on line in 1956 producing 50MW (thermal). More prosaically, Chapelcross in Dumfriesshire when it started in February 1959 produced 30MW (thermal).

As against this, DFR was planned with 60MW (thermal) in mind.

At the heart of any reactor is the core containing the fuel of enriched uranium (usually several tons) generally in the form of fuel rods. The temperature at this core can reach around 300°C. This heat is caused by the spontaneous fission of the enriched uranium. For a chain reaction – a continuous nuclear 'fire' (scientists cringe at the word 'fire' in connection with nuclear power) – there has to be sufficient uranium to ensure that any neutron liberated from the nucleus of the atom stands a good chance of being absorbed by another uranium atom and thus bring about another

fission – forging the next link in the chain and so fourth. This chain reaction will continue indefinitely until there is not enough fissionable material left. If this process is uncontrolled, where one neutron liberates two and in turn they liberate four and so on, then the number of breakdowns would rise rapidly (within millionths of a second) and lead to an explosion.

Given sufficient fuel a chain reaction can proceed in an orderly fashion. Too little fuel and the reaction would simply come to a halt; too much and a core meltdown could occur; when it is at a point where the chain reaction just keeps going then it is said to be at critical size.

These control rods, the second aspect of the nuclear reactor after the core, actually were in themselves controlled by arms that hung down the sides of the reactor vessel, stemming from its roof, fixed in a cantilever arrangement with an extended leg stretching horizontally from the base of each arm under the vessel and each leg having an egg-cup shape receptacle on its extremity that held the actual control rod. An electro-magnetic clutch operated on the circuit so that an emergency shut down could be effected by simply releasing the clutch and then the carriage and fuel elements would fall out under gravity. There were two of these control rods between each star – thus a total of 120 fuel rods making up the main control element. There was also the facility to drop in boron rods from the top if need be but, under normal circumstances, the fuel rods sufficed to permit precise regulation of the system.

Around this core (a mere 21 inches by 21 inches) the third aspect of the reactor was constructed. This was a breeder blanket of 1,872 rods of natural uranium, each rod weighing 80lbs, which was wrapped round to deflect the neutrons back into the core. This was the reflector part of the apparatus. Unplated niobium and vanadium were chosen as the metals for the fuel containers and the fuel itself was in the form of pellets.

The core, clearly showing the 'Chinese chequer board' configuration. Part of the core of DFR was shaped as a six-pointed star (exactly in the fashion of a Chinese chequer board – peg slots and all) in which 225 fuel element rods were placed. Between the six points of the star, in what would have been empty space in the Chinese chequer board – the triangular space in-between – were placed the twelve control rods (each capable of containing ten fuel rods in themselves) that could be dropped out of or raised up into the core as required, thus either damping down the fission reaction or encouraging it as required.

DFR's rotating shields. Two eccentrically rotating shields that could act independently of each other provided the protection on top of the reactor. The inner shield was mounted within the outer and by accurately rotating the shields a refuelling hole could be sited over each of the fuel element positions as different aspects of the top of the core came into view. A device similar to a periscope (but looking downwards) permitted visual examination of the position of each hole. Initially the core was loaded by hand before NaK was introduced into the system.

The fuel elements were stored in such a fashion as permitted only four to be accessed at a time – this as a safeguard against the unlikely happening of inadvertent criticality. Each fuel rod had its own unique number and its history attached to it and two supervisors had to independently check upon its insertion into the reactor.

The original intention was to hold the fuel elements in place from the top but trials demonstrated they were subject to vibration and a base support plate was used as well. Spiral fins on the cladding of each element ensured the hub of each remained aloof from its neighbour and thus overheating of the cladding was avoided.

NaK was one of the main differences between DFR and the other reactors of the day. It was the coolant (another aspect of a reactor) for the system and it was an alloy of sodium and potassium (70% to 30%). This substance starts to freeze at 50 degrees Celsius. It is a difficult and dangerous substance within itself and added to the complexities of the operation, as it required to be heated at all times.

As well as this, NaK is extremely efficient in transferring heat. It was circulated through the reactor by electro-magnetic pumps and through the 24 heat exchanger units arranged radially around the core. It flowed from top to bottom to ensure the base gained the greater heat. A downside to this arrangement was that any gas bubbles formed could be trapped as they attempted to rise against the flow.

The first two coolant systems of DFR used NaK and the third was the final fresh water circuit that transferred the heat in the heat exchanger building.

Temperature gauges kept check on the core temperature and the

Part of the heat exchanger building. The inner circuit (the one wholly inside the shielding) carried the extremely hot and radioactive NaK that went through the core; this circuit yielded its heat to the second circuit that remained non-radioactive and led into the heat exchanger building where it met the third, fresh water circuit from which the steam was raised; steam that could be dumped to sea or used to drive the turbo-alternator.

heat in the surrounding NaK. Pressure gauges reported upon the pressure of the nitrogen blanket that surrounded the liquid metal. Generally the checking instrumentation was mounted directly over the reactor with neutron detectors placed within the graphite surround to measure the level of radiation. The inert gas nitrogen acted as a seal over the NaK; this gas was changed to argon in 1962 because nitrogen can embrittle steel at high temperatures and, whilst even the massive temperatures raised by DFR were not enough to reach this point it was appreciated that future reactors would do so. So the more expensive argon was used in DFR to study its reaction.

Most of the problems of DFR involved the liquid coolant. All this came in drums to the site. Some drums held mixes of the alloy of sodium and potassium whilst others contained only pure sodium. Sodium at ordinary

Shift Manager Geoff Cullington at the DFR control desk. The whole of the operation was mimicked on the master control board. Each part of the operation had circuits leading back to the main panel and the fascia was a mass of dials, tracers, switches and buttons. The main switch permitted the control rods to be handled one group at a time but there was an emergency switch for an immediate shutdown that activated the release mechanism for all the control rods simultaneously.

temperatures is a solid, and these metal drums had to be gently heated in electric 'muffs' that were wrapped around. No water was permitted in the temperature-controlled room where this operation was carried out and all operators connected with it wore specially designed protective clothing. The potassium metal was dealt with in a similar fashion, the muff bringing it to the same temperature as the sodium so the two could be impelled into the mixing tank before being filtered and pumped onto the storage vessels. Unfortunately there were considerable levels of impurities within the coolant delivered to the site. The drums containing the alloy were severely contaminated with oil and this was to cause frequent clogging of filters and even blockages of pipes. Often the blockages were too severe to simply be rodded through and then the pipe sections had to be cut and replaced.

The design intention had been to remove impurity from the coolant using cold traps. Flow through these traps occurred only when the coolant in the main circuit exceeded 70% of the full design value and, below this, the cold traps were ineffective. It was not appreciated, however, that at about a 70% flow the nitrogen gas became subject to severe entrainment where bubbles of the gas would become trapped in the coolant flow. This effectively put the cold traps out of service. The coolant clean-up problem, although much improved by then, took until 1961 before it was finally ended.

To protect against a loss of coolant the primary system was built using all welded construction with neither valves nor gland seals below the surface of the liquid metal. The pumps themselves were welded into the main pipe-work. A leak jacket surrounded the primary system. Sufficient NaK was available in the primary circuit to ensure that if the coolant leaked into the jacket, the core would remain submerged – and the advantage of having so many circuits meant that the loss of a single pump would not cause a serious problem.

All this added to the overall cost, as did the amount of reserve equipment built into the system, for example. There were twelve diesel driven alternators in the Pump House – plus six others on stand-by.

And watching, standing like an aloof sentinel over all this new and fledgling technology, was the Goliath crane; a magnificent example of traditional Scottish engineering and craftsmanship. Its purpose was to move the giant flasks, containing the fuel elements, and position them with precision over the reactor top. The crane had a lifting capacity of 25 tons and was built in a shape somewhat resembling an outsized goalpost frame. It rotated through 360 degrees on a rail that encircled the perimeter of the reactor-top floor. On the 'cross-bar' was another rail on which was mounted a trolley crane grasp. Thus, by manipulation of both the crane's moving functions, every part of the floor, approximately one-third of an acre in size, was made accessible.

And, whilst all this was going on in Dounreay, how did Thurso fare?

Alistair Cowie pictured with the Goliath crane following its recent refurbishment.

EARLY OBJECTIVES OF DFR

- To check the overall engineering design and, after appropriate modification where required, to establish a routine operating plan.
- To check reactor physics parameters, initially to gain confidence that important basic assumptions underlying DFR design and operating procedures were sound.
- To investigate in great detail the reactivity and stability of the reactor over the whole operating range.
- To check and then to improve the DFR fuel element and, later, the candidate fuel elements for PFR.
- To provide information and facilities necessary for fulfilling the role of a fast materials test reactor.
- In addition, information was required for the benefit of fast reactor general technological development.

In practice these objectives had considerable interactions as well as overlaps in timing. This was to some extent the result of the unforeseen commissioning problems that required adjustments to the planned programme. Amongst the teams involved there was a strong underlying spirit of understanding and considerable mutual support amongst the individuals concerned.

The principal reactor physics objectives were:-
- To check the calculated values of those reactor parameters that had implications for safety or operational procedures.
- To determine the measure of agreement between calculation and experiment of reaction rates in accessible parts of DFR and thereby assess the confidence to be placed in calculated values for the inaccessible regions.
- To investigate those reactions that, in Zeus (an earlier UKAEA reactor), had shown disagreement between calculation and experiment.
- To make measurements that were not practicable in Zeus such as the effectiveness of shielding.

JONATHON KIRK

Jonathon Kirk, pictured on the left beside project manager Warren Jones.

Jonathon Kirk epitomizes much of the history of Dounreay. He began his career at the plant when DFR was being built and spent his whole time with it. His first task was as shift manager and he was instructed to get as close to the plant as possible whilst it was under construction in order to learn as much about it as possible and also to use this knowledge to assist in the preparation of the operation manual.

Jonathon eventually retired as head of DFR Decommissioning but remained active in a consultancy role. He is still in touch with Americans he befriended in his working years when he visited the States to advise on the decommissioning of reactors there.

Like so many others who migrated to Caithness, Jonathon stayed a little longer than ever he thought he would. In his early years with Dounreay he applied for another job down south and, returning from the interview, he was struck by the thought, 'Why do I want another job?'

It was all in Caithness; exciting work at the cutting edge of a new technology, a splendid environment to raise children, excellent schooling, beautiful countryside, sociable and friendly people.

He never applied for another job again.

NUCLEAR FUELS

Naturally occurring uranium is a poor material to use for a chain reaction because it mainly consists of the isotope uranium-238 that absorbs neutrons without undergoing fission (except at high energies). Fortunately uranium is relatively abundant and can readily be mined in the form of ore. It then needs to be prepared in such a manner to ensure the highly fissionable isotope, uranium-235, is isolated. The task of dividing out this isotope from uranium-238 is difficult (uranium-235 normally represents only 0.7% of all uranium sources) and is normally carried out by gas centrifuges after the uranium is converted into the gas uranium hexafluoride.

STRUCTURE OF NUCLEAR REACTORS

A nuclear reactor is a unit designed to contain all the equipment and material required to produce and sustain nuclear fission in a controlled fashion.

There are, usually, six elements to a reactor; the fuel, the controlling mechanism, the moderator, the reflector, the coolant and the shielding.

The controlling mechanism usually consists of rods of cadmium. Cadmium absorbs neutrons without bouncing them back or re-emitting them and is thus an ideal material for managing the fission process.

Since the speed of neutrons emitted in the act of fission is extremely fast (they can travel at 14,000 kilometers per second) ands as they are very penetrating they could easily escape the core of the reactor before they collide with any other nucleus, consequently they have to be slowed – or moderated as the term is. The thermal reactor has a moderator around the core that slows the neutrons until they approach the average speed of the surrounding particles. Often the moderator is of the same material as the coolant. Reactors without a moderator are termed 'fast reactors.'

The reflector is an area of material that surrounds the core. Its function is to bounce back neutrons from the core and keep the power density stable within a range.

The coolant circulates through the core removing the heat build-up and taking that heat onto another circuit where the heat can be used to drive generators.

Lastly there is that most important part of the reactor, the shield. Although not a working part, the massive shielding that surrounds such protects from the powerful and piercing rays being manufactured within since fission and radioactive decay produce both neutrons and gamma rays. Thus the shield is composed of solid concrete, several feet thick and interwoven or lined with lead and steel.

USES OF REACTORS

The most common use for reactors is the production of electricity. Initially though they were used for the manufacture of materials for nuclear weapons. Another military use that reactors have been put to is the powering of marine vessels including submarines. More constructively they are also used to produce radioisotopes for medical applications as well as being used for scientific experimental and research purposes.

Chapter Twelve
Thor's Town

Thurso castle from the mouth of the river.

Ormlie Lodge.

Part of the remains of old St Peter's Church.

The war memorial looking down Sir George Street.

Scrabster Harbour.

There is a calm beauty about Thurso. The river runs quietly to the sea through civilised scenery with pleasant houses set tactfully well back from the bank permitting room for a path and, hence, providing the prospect of a gentle country stroll after Sunday lunch. The streets are tidy and well kept and the War Memorial – Victory holding aloft her poignant sword as she gazes south down Sir George Street – dominates the approach into the centre. The buildings are trim and there is an air of quiet bustle around the pedestrianised centre.

Everything is neat and orderly on a small scale – the remains of the old St. Peter's Church are a miniature delight and the beach is not large but is clean and attractive. You are surprised to learn that some of the best surfing in Britain is available at the mouth of the river – international surfing championships have been held there and will be again. And where else can you get such clean, fresh air, a view to the misty Orkneys and an occasional glimpse of the majesty of the universe when the shy lady of the Aurora Borealis blushingly raises her veil at night.

A feeling of permanency and timelessness pervades the town. The sophisticate may joke about Thurso being so far from civilisation (even today the nearest Marks and Spencer's store is over 100 road miles south) but the wise child of Thor (Thurso people are called 'Thorkies' whilst 'Golah' can be used for a Caithness citizen) will say nothing but give a sad shake of the head when the slick one turns away.

Surprisingly though, most of the town is fairly recent.

In a short nine years Thurso swelled from 3,350 of a population in 1955 to 9,190 by 1964 – the highest percentage any existing town has increased by in the UK. The largest jump was in 1958 when some 2,800 'atomics' arrived. 'Atomics' was the name given to the newcomers associated with Dounreay. These tended to be young newly-weds attracted, amongst other things, by the promise of the excellent rented accommodation offered by the UKAEA and the added carrot of having all their removal and travel expenses paid. Les King and his wife were one such couple. Born in 1938 in Milton-of-Campsie, a village near Glasgow, Les had been told he'd have to wait years for a council house for himself and his wife (they were living with his in-laws at the time).

Les could not believe at first that he would get the immediate rental of a four bedroom semi-detached house built with 1960's standard all mod cons when he joined Dounreay as a turner. He jumped at the chance. His wife later became manageress at the Social Club in Dounreay. Les retired in 1994 but Dounreay still provides employment for his son and grandson.

Les's experience was typical of many and typical also was the way in which he was accepted by the local community and how he adapted into it and respected the environment he had come to live in. Although integration of the new atomics with the older Thurso people was relatively smooth – partly due to the sound, common sense of the locals and the fine appreciation shown by the incomers as to what they had settled in – it was hampered, at least initially, by the high turnover of staff at Dounreay. This was because of the flexible nature of the work and the fact that many individuals simply wanted work for a while before returning to their roots.

Integration too tended to be class based. Many of the new-comers were from the professional and middle-classes and they took the initiative in setting up clubs and societies in Thurso which drew in some indigenous people but left many untouched. There is little evidence of intermarriage between the two strands of the community in the early days. However, Provost Sinclair could state, in 1961, 'We are all locals now;' a little premature but not by much.

North Highland College.

One of the factors that eased integration was the mix of children in the schools. The population drift to the coast was well established prior to Dounreay and a school building programme was essential anyway but, as with so many other facets of life and society, Dounreay accelerated the process; to blame Dounreay for the dereliction of some of the rural areas left behind (as some did) is entirely unfair. Thurso was the main beneficiary. Two new primary schools were established; one in Castlegreen and the other at Mount Pleasant and, in 1958, Thurso High (room for 480 pupils) was opened (replacing Miller Academy as the senior school whilst that academy reverted to a primary one) and almost immediately extended to care for the increasing numbers. There have been other extensions since. Because of the nature of the Caithness people, education has always been an important and respected factor with them (hence the higher than average number of Caithnesians who attend university). In 1964, the Thurso Technical College, which had been set up in 1956, moved into an attractive building at Ormlie with room for 1,000 students. UKAEA supplied the vast majority of the equipment, technical apparatus and, especially in the beginning, many of the lecturers and instructors – and the majority of students. Today, the college (now renamed and expanded into the North Highland College) remains heavily involved with Dounreay but not as dependent on it and now furnishes a full range of courses in all disciplines.

On top of that the UKAEA established an apprentice hostel within the atomic housing estate in addition to its main hostel at Ormlie Lodge – the Lodge being a large private house that had been extended to accommodate 250 employees. 'Viewfirth', another large house, had also been purchased to act as a social and sports club for Dounreay workers (a similar club was established in Wick). All in all the Authority were paying over 25% of the rates of Thurso at the time.

Up to the arrival of the atomics there was a marked imbalance in the population as the young aged between 16 and 24 tended to head south seeking work. A few years after the start of Dounreay there was, understandably, a boom in the age group 25 to 40 and, also understandably, another boom in the 0 to 5 age group as the young couples arriving started their families: soon the population under 15 represented over 31%.

The emigration of young locals did not stop immediately however and the phenomenon ran concurrent with the heavy immigration pattern. The influx of young males also changed the balance between the sexes, as, more than their male counterparts, local girls had tended to stay at home. From 1960 onwards the emigration of the young finally halted as Dounreay provided increasing opportunities.

By 1966, the year when construction of the prototype fast reactor commenced, more and more atomics stayed and today, almost fifty years after Les first arrived, the distinction between local and atomic and even between Scot and non-Scot (some 50% of the incomers were from England, Ireland or Wales) is indiscernible.

Thurso itself was not dying before the advent of Dounreay – a point made forcibly at the time by Provost Sinclair – it would have remained a small market town, but Dounreay stopped the population decline, moved the balance to a younger generation and accelerated the birth-rate and, for many a year at least, stopped the drift south of the new generation. Nevertheless, as a government report of the time put it, 'Caithness had a declining primary sector and little manufacturing industry' and suffered from 'an under-utilisation of land resources.'

Part of the success of the integration of Dounreay lay in the fact that, contrary to the belief of many, people in Thurso and Caithness were more sophisticated in their outlook and more cosmopolitan than such small and isolated communities could be expected to be. They had after all dealt with the great influx of people and nationalities at the high time of the herring industry (a Danish consul still resides in Wick – Malcolm Bremner) and had experienced first-hand business dealings on an international scale. Caithness had also played host to innumerable people of all nationalities during the years of war and against this the individuals who came north as atomics were few and from (relatively) the same cultural background.

The reward for this was marked. If unemployment had been 17.8% one black winter in the early fifties, it fell to 2.5% between '55 and '58. The higher rates of pay at Dounreay (£40 per week for unskilled up to £80 for skilled – about 30% above the average) ensured that shop turnovers were well up also – something like 40% higher. And the security of employment played a vital part; the people coming in were prepared to spend because they knew the jobs were safe, government ones.

As time passed, more of the jobs went to local labour; 63% by 1963, 69% by 1967. Most of the local workforce came from Thurso or the nearby villages of Castletown, Halkirk or Reay but some came from Wick and not a few journeyed from villages in the south of Caithness and even from such as Tongue – along the north coast west of Caithness into Sutherland. Initially most of the locals employed were either unskilled or semi-skilled but as the UKAEA launched its various training schemes this raised the standard of jobs being performed by Caithnesians.

So Thurso and its environs were prospering. New homes were going up; between 1956 and 1968 some 1800 new houses were erected with the majority being directly contributed by the UKAEA and the bulk of the rest by the local authority and Scottish Special Housing. Initially it had been hoped to integrate the atomic houses with local developments but this would have proved both too costly and impracticable; so the atomics did find themselves segregated into the new housing schemes. This rush of building also acted as a stimulus to private builders and in the first ten years of Dounreay almost fifty private homes were constructed compared to one during the previous ten. In contrast, Wick hardly grew. Any house building there was mainly in the redevelopment of clearance sites. Donald Carmichael had the privilege of putting proposals forward to name the new streets in Thurso. He drew on the old Viking Sagas for his inspiration. Thus Thurso rejoices in having Thorfinn, St. Olaf, St. Magnus and Hakon streets amongst others. But the immediate effect of Dounreay was not always for the good everywhere.

St Olaf Road.

Chapter Thirteen
Growing Pains

Dounreay offered high paid and secure jobs to locals – and there were plenty. Labour left the land and, more crucially, the sea to sign on with the UKAEA.

Farming had been declining anyway – not in total output but in numbers employed. Amalgamation, mechanisation, the trend towards rearing and breeding animals and the greater specialisation of labour itself had drastically reduced the requirement for workers. Dounreay merely accelerated this tendency. Farmers themselves expressed their concerns about the increasing difficulty in obtaining labour and this all hastened the introduction of dedicated machinery to the county's farms. In the twenty years following the beginnings of Dounreay numbers employed in farming fell from over 1500 to just over 500.

Dounreay had, however, a more immediate and more beneficial effect on crofting. Prior to Dounreay the small croft had provided a very limited living. Most crofters either had to seek part-time work within the area or, as often was the case if they were married, one partner would work outwith the county whilst the other tended the croft. The sons and daughters of such a union were generally forced south in search of work. Dounreay solved this almost immediately with one partner taking employment with the Authority and with sons and daughters duly joining in their turn. Thus Dounreay helped maintain the underlying tenet of the crofting system.

Respecting fishing, Dounreay had a more immediate and profound impact. Gwynedd County Planning Department in Wales had faced a similar situation to Dounreay and their view had been pessimistic; concerning the siting of a power station in their locale they had written, 'The long term effect of a major construction scheme is to help prevent the growth of more stable industries because of the impact on local wage levels and labour supply.' Some, back in the middle fifties, took a similar view in regard to the run down of fishing in Caithness and the impact of Dounreay. However, what was relevant for Gwynedd did not apply to Caithness where the collapse of the herring industry meant that only 400 were actually employed in Wick in 1951 against the thousands that used to swarm through its streets to the quayside. The key word in the Gwynedd report had been 'stable' and few Caithness industries could boast of being that.

Thurso had been a white fish port but as larger boats had come into use the town found itself losing out to Scrabster (a small port only two miles outside Thurso). Scrabster had natural tidal advantages and was more cosmopolitan in that Thurso was basically used by Thurso owned boats whereas Scrabster was used by many who came from much further afield; in Thurso larger boats could not always use the harbour and the river was susceptible to silting. Scrabster's rise could be traced to the end of the First World War when boats from all round the coast began to land fish there. However, with the start of construction work at Dounreay, fishers of all types took advantage of the high wages offered and the convenience and comfort of having a secure land job. Some, as Provost Sinclair had maintained they would, did indeed return to the sea but most were contented with Dounreay. The majority were younger men a few of whom, in time, would have been looking to own their own boats. Although landings at Scrabster continued to increase for a while this was due to boats from further afield using it as a harbour. Local Scrabster

Watercolour of Thurso's ' Fisherbiggins' by local artist Jack Saxon (reproduced by kind permission of Roger Saxon).

The oil distribution centre at Scrabster Harbour.

boats declined from 124 in 1954 to only 16 by 1958. Scrabster, however, received a further boost when the Shell-Mex Oil Company decided to use the harbour as an oil distributing facility in 1957 to serve the Far North – an indirect and welcome consequence of Dounreay.

The other aspect the immigrants brought with them into the county, for better or for worse, was a heightened political awareness. Broadly, the political machinery of Caithness, such as it was, had been run by conservative businessmen who dealt with council and local affairs whilst keeping a nominal distance from party allegiance. The landed gentry (who were relatively liberal in their thinking) represented the county at national level. Provost John Sinclair was one of the few politicians in the community who came from a working-class background.

However, the Dounreay immigrants brought with them trade unionism and socialism. The Dounreay management were relaxed about the formation of unions (a well run union is always a handy management asset) and a branch of the Institute of Professional Civil Servants was quickly established. Later on the Transport and General Workers' Union located a full time officer in Wick and The Amalgamated Union of Electrical Workers also established a presence.

All this changed the political outlook. There was an increase in working class representation on such bodies as had been almost exclusively middle and upper class dominated. The Careers Council, the local Health Board and the Education Committee were all examples of such institutions that broadened their base. The Thurso and District Trades Council was born in the mid-sixties and the Labour Party, reformed in the early sixties (the Canisbay Labour Party was one of the oldest in Scotland), won its first ever victory in Caithness when Robert MacLennan, a Glasgow man, inherited Sir David's domain in the 1966 election.

The Scottish National Party organised itself in the county, again mainly as a result of the more politically active incomers and all this upsurge of aggressive political activity led to some diminution of the influence of the older and generally landed establishment. A few atomics even began standing as councillors and the first atomic provost of Thurso was Tom Pollok in 1970.

A longer term political result was the gradual weaning of power from the old county town of Wick, in the east of Caithness and facing the Continent, to Thurso, facing the Orkneys and beyond. This mirrored the economic current with Wick in a slow but steady decline in contrast to the rise in prosperity in the West. This direction was general rather than specific nor, as with so much, was it entirely due to Dounreay but again the nuclear plant played its part. Wick is the old county town, a town of rich and turbulent history, but the main road through the county, the A9, now runs to Thurso and the local branch of the Highlands and Islands Enterprise Company has established its headquarters there.

If politics expanded so also did religion broaden its base. Prior to Dounreay there were few Roman Catholics in Caithness. Most Caithnesians were Church of Scotland although there was a goodly mix of Quakers, Methodists, Episcopalians, Congregationalists and Unitarians. The arrival of a number of Catholics led to a new chapel, St. Anne's Church, being adjacent to the atomic estate. As ever, the good sense of the Caithness people ensured and ensures that religious differences are not an issue.

Health facilities also expanded and improved and with more specialised treatments available less people had to travel to Inverness.

Development was the key word in the county.

Chapter Fourteen
Developing

Sir William Smith's birthplace was commemorated on his 100th birthday.

Dounreay was never to achieve all that Sir David Robertson had hoped for at its inauguration; it was never to act as a catalyst for other industries and businesses to locate to Caithness and spark a mini-industrial revolution in the Highlands. Nevertheless it did encourage a spread of activities within the county. By the early sixties there was an air of bustle about Thurso as roads improved, new schools opened, a new water scheme started, and houses seemed to leap up.

Shop turnovers soared. Some commentators criticised the existing shops of Thurso as being slow to respond to the growing market but they forgot that most of those who came to work at Dounreay were not permanent residents and the shopkeeper had to earn the money before indulging in expansion. The local Savings Bank was quick off its mark however in increasing its staff from three to eleven within a short space of time.

Rotterdam Street.

However, in the first few years of operation, Thurso did gain three ladies shops, one draper, a furniture store, two painters and decorators, an electrical appliance shop, a garage and a vital ladies hair-dressing salon.

By the mid-sixties rateable values were 155% above the 1955 figure as there came a surge of new shops – and new types of shops at that; fashion boutiques, health food stores, gift shops, model shops, toy shops, – all catering to the demand of the growing number of atomics. Many of them were opened by atomics themselves. With well-paid and secure jobs and with capital behind them from selling up further south, some of the incomers or, rather, their spouses established such stores as gift shops, teashops, card shops, art shops, health stores, toyshops, fashion shops and even a dedicated bookshop whilst the main bread winner worked at Dounreay. Existing stores expanded and widened their services and stock. Further specialist shops appeared such as a photographer, a florist, a music shop and a dry cleaner. New motor dealerships opened as did new taxi firms and, naturally, so also did more dress shops and ladies hairdressers. Odd as it may seem now, there were protests over Woolworth's opening a branch in the High Street in 1962.

Other expansions found themselves with a better welcome; hotels inaugurated cocktail bars and more cafes and restaurants popped into being as well as new fish and chip shops and Thurso finally knew it had entered the world when a bookmaker established himself.

Leisure activities sprouted. In short order a bridge club, a badminton club, and a sailing club were set up (the Snipe World Championships have been held in Thurso Bay); there was also the innovative Caithness Field Club whose objective was to research and study local geology, archaeology, geography, history and all aspects of

Yachts becalmed in Thurso Bay with Dunnet Head in the background.

The existing organisations such as the Scouts, the Guides, the Sea-Army Cadets and the several youth clubs all were boosted by the entry of the incomers – including the ever-reliable Salvation Army. In this illustrious list, the Boys Brigade deserves special mention since its founder, Sir William Smith, was born in Thurso in 1854. Pennyland House, his birthplace, is still used today as a private residence.

Other, less common sporting activities developed as well. Judo, sub-aqua, cycling, surfing, sea angling, and sand yachting all boomed. If Dounreay was about energy, the social scene in Thurso changed as a fresh social energy swept through it. Cultural activities flourished. The new schools encouraged the arts and there were drama and film societies. The Annual Gala prospered achieving over £2,000 per annum for several years running. For a town of its size there sure was a lot going on.

Finally, helped by the keenly interested Donald Carmichael who was one of those afflicted with the disease, golf (or, should that be 'Golf') began again at Reay and the Thurso course was renovated and extended – in time for the extra tourists who were now finding their path into the far north. The families and friends of the newly established came up on social visits and, obligatory, had to view John O'Groats and, at a later date, had to see the famous glass factory at Wick (sadly, no longer extant). It would not be correct to say that tourism boomed but it certainly increased considerably as a result of the atomics. In combination with the added passenger numbers Dounreay was providing it with anyway, this increase in tourism helped strengthen the case for the retention of the Far North rail link to Inverness. Bus services also improved and, later, Highland Omnibuses were to be toasted at a special event held by the Authority for the way they had handled the increasing demands in getting workers into and out of Dounreay in all sorts of conditions.

And, apart from all these goings-on which all could be considered indirect effects of Dounreay, there were also new commercial concerns more directly related to Dounreay's activities.

the county's varied flora and fauna. A rugby club began and, longer term, dedicated enthusiasts finally succeeded in opening a small indoor swimming pool in 1967. Thurso Swimming Club was to gain particular distinction in competitions.

These phenomena were not solely the province of the atomics nor did these associations and societies arise through their efforts alone. The swimming pool was a collaborative effort involving the whole community (£7,000 was donated by the public) – in which, by that time, there was less distinction between newcomer and indigenous born.

Reay Golf Club.

Chapter Fifteen
Other Works

NRTE Vulcan is shown in the foreground.

The most immediate venture to establish itself with relevance to Dounreay was also Dounreay's most immediate neighbour. The Admiralty's shore base 'HMS Vulcan' adjoined Dounreay and the Admiralty set up an experimental reactor plant there, under the management of Rolls Royce, specifically to work on the development of nuclear engines for submarines and the training of nuclear sub-mariners. The vast majority engaged in the beginning were naval personnel but a few locals were employed as unskilled workers or as fitters. The Admiralty could argue that they would have needed such a station irrespective of the existence of Dounreay but, there is no doubt, Dounreay was the main factor in situating that facility in Caithness.

Today the plant has been renamed NRTE (Naval Reactor Test Establishment) Vulcan and, although the Ministry of Defence retain control, few navy men are employed. Rolls Royce still retains almost 300 individuals and local contractors are always to be found working there.

Dounreay was also important in the setting up of a number of small engineering firms in the county. They did not depend solely for their business on the UKAEA but the work the Authority placed with them often proved essential. Ex-Dounreay workers started a number of these companies and one or two such firms have even gone on to gain an enviable international reputation.

Another successful spin-off, perhaps a more direct spin-off, was the centralization of the UKAEA pension fund administration in Thurso. By 1963,

with an expanding national workforce, increased rules and regulations and the growing complexity of superannuation schemes in general, UKAEA took the decision to centralize this amenity. The Sinclair Family Trust was redeveloping the old High Street at that time. Part of that expansion included the construction of Tollemache House that was selected by the UKAEA as the ideal site to house their newly centralised staff pension scheme. The arrival of the fund was looked upon as a further compliment to the area that had already adapted so well to new ways and new skills.

In 1998 the facility transferred to Brownhill Lodge. A staff of thirty, of which twelve are part-time, still work there under Thurso born manager

Tollemache House.

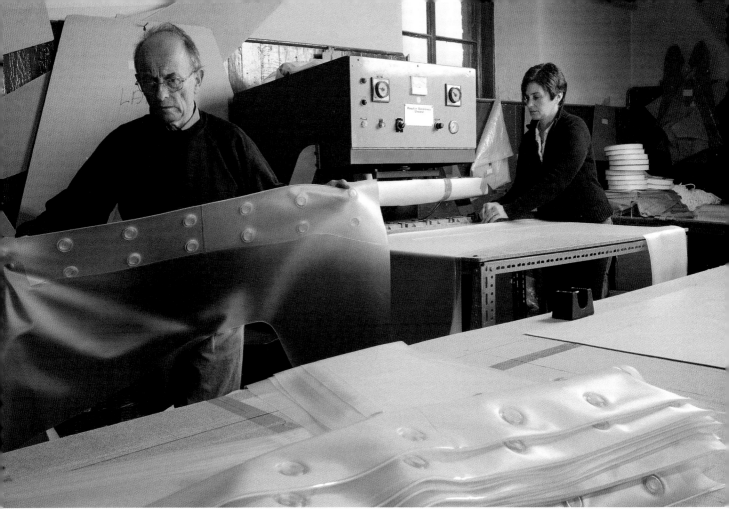

Peter Mackenzie and Annette Mcarthy of Stephen's Plastics.

Alan Cormack. Together they look after over 50,000 pensions. As well as UKAEA staff they care for the pension funds of staff from British Nuclear Fuels, the radiation division of the Health Protection Agency, the Ministry of Defence and RWE Nukem – the latter a German company (the initials stand for Rhine and Westphalia Electricity) – and in the spring of 2006 were awarded the contract of managing the NDA site-wide pension scheme that is intended to become operable once site licence companies are established at Dounreay.

A more complicated venture to set up though was AGM Batteries. This company was a joint endeavour started by AEA Technology (in itself set up at a time when the UKAEA was being encouraged to privatise and diverse), the Japan Storage Battery Company and Mitsubishi Materials Corporation. The company began production in early 2000 from Thurso Business Park and commenced manufacture two years later. The company soared to success on the back of its world leading technology (it has now expanded to premises in Glengarnock and also to Golspie). Its specialised lightweight batteries proved much in demand for use in space satellites and in medical applications. The Business Park itself is a recent prodigy and was established primarily to counteract what was envisaged as the run-down of Dounreay in the wake of the closure of the fast reactor programme.

It may well be, however, that the company which set up in Caithness and came closest to Sir David Robertson's idea of Dounreay attracting in new industry was (and is) Stephen's Plastics based in Halkirk.

Halkirk is a distinctive village in its design. The name derives from the Old Norse 'Hakirkja' meaning High Church. Sir John Sinclair laid out the modern village in grid plan in 1803 on land then considered unsuitable for ploughing. Its closeness to Thurso could well have meant that it merely became a dormer zone for the town but the enterprise of the small village has blessed it with no less than four manufacturing companies.

Stephen's Plastics of Wiltshire established its Halkirk branch in September 1959, and had the distinction of being the first subsidiary industry brought into being as a direct result of Dounreay. Its purpose was to manufacture specialist plastic protective clothing for the nuclear industry from simple aprons up to full body covering. Mr. E. G. Hawkins, a specialist in this field, was released by Dounreay to take over the day-to-day running of the company. Stephen's, with a steady market into Dounreay, hoped to expand their activities throughout Scotland and especially into the agricultural and fishing industries – the firm at that time was the largest manufacturer of silage and hay rick covers in the world. Not daunted by Donald Carmichael's praising of his tenacity and courage in setting up in Caithness, Mr. Stephen, an ex-army man, looked forward to many years of work in the area.

Although the company does not employ as many as it one time did and went through a management buy-out in 2002, it still employs 13 and still serves the nuclear industry with Sellafield now being its largest customer – although Dounreay orders 3,000 over-suits per annum as well as boiler suits, jackets, trousers, hoods, boots and overshoes (there are over fifty standard items in the firm's range). The work is intricate starting with the design of the specialist clothing required through to the conception and engineering of the shaping and heat-sealing units needed to produce the item. Similar heat sealers are used in other industries, such as the processed food industry, but, unlike them, every seal has to be perfect because of the slight danger of airborne contamination in hazardous areas. Today its managing director is Mr. Andrew Marshall and the running of it is in the experienced hands of Liz Swanson and Peter Mackenzie.

Apart from these companies, with their direct links to Dounreay, many other companies have profited by Dounreay and not a few have been established to take advantage of the presence of Dounreay although much of their trading has and is elsewhere.

And with all this grand upheaval of life and business going on around it, Dounreay was up and running.

Chapter Sixteen
Up, Running and Reprocessing

Dounreay was in its heyday. DFR was on song, employment and earnings were high, and the community was thriving.

Around the dome all was bustle as scientists and engineers probed, studied and played with the new technology. Because Dounreay was a research and development complex, there were more than 180 separate facilities, each of which could include several buildings. The whole site was self-contained. There was the plant room, the extractor ventilating plant, the administrative block, the active handling bay (dealing with irradiated materials), the fitting shop, and the pump house with its coolant tower. Fuel was manufactured, loaded to the reactor, removed to the cooling ponds, sent for reprocessing and then machined into billets from whence it was again made into fuel.

This cycle is termed the fast reactor fuel cycle where the fuel utilization is optimised. It requires that the plutonium created in the depleted uranium within the breeder elements is recovered for re-use.

Unfortunately this sequence (of necessity) also produced radioactive waste (as a liquor) and therefore waste storage and disposal plants were required.

Research reactor fuel units were made in an unromantic block building. In the beginning this was solely carried out in connection with DMTR but, later, other similar reactors from different countries purchased fuel from here. The fuel billets generally weighed around 5lbs and would be molten in the furnaces and rolled with aluminium to manufacture the finished article: ultra-sound was one technique used to test the integrity of materials. Apart from fuel this unit also produced mildly radioactive tracer material for medical use and irradiated materials for medical purposes provided 10 million treatments for European cancer sufferers. By the time it closed in March 2004 over 10,000 fuel elements had been produced over the years.

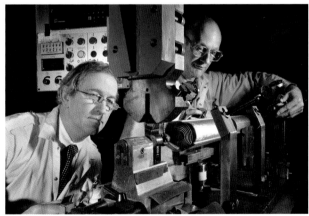

Calder Bain and Alan Sinclair involved in the manufacture of a fuel element.

The factory that acted as the interface unit between reprocessing the spent fuel and the manufacture of new fuel elements recovered uranyl-nitrate in liquid form from the reprocessing plants (via the pipe bridge) and converted that into billets of highly enriched uranium. The fuel recovery plant, as it was known, was considered essential back in the days when uranium was looked on as almost priceless and every gram had to be recovered; it was the accountants who monitored uranium loss in those days and not the physicists – hence the term nuclear materials accountancy.

The Chemical Group became known as the Fuel Cycle Area. This is where the reprocessing of the spent fuel occurred – with a special building

reprocessing MTR fuel and another building the fast reactor fuel. Some of the monitoring and measuring equipment used here was so sensitive that it had to be shielded from natural background radiation (this shielding applied to a lot of equipment, particularly in Health Physics). The steel used to guard such equipment came from pre-1945 warships that had been broken up and whose steel would be free of any residue of radiation caused by the nuclear bomb tests of that era.

By today's standards the initial operation for MTR fuel was small-scale. The dissolving vessel had a capacity of only 150 litres. Nevertheless it got through a power of work. The incoming used fuel elements were cropped in a concrete lined pond under the water (the water acting both as an absorber of heat and radioactivity) and the cut pieces remotely loaded onto an elevator, the buckets of which carried the pieces into the dissolving 'pot.'

Once full, hydraulic rams sealed the top of this pot as the acids worked. A liquid of highly enriched uranyl nitrate was extracted from this and the acidic and radioactive residue (the raffinate) was then stored in underground tanks.

The fast reactor reprocessing works initially reprocessed DFR fuel in a similar fashion to the research reactor reprocessing plant. After DFR's closure it was rebuilt and modified to reprocess plutonium and uranium oxide fuel from PFR. This plutonium-bearing fuels reprocessing facility was sometimes called the oxide plant (because the incoming irradiated PFR fuel had plutonium oxide as its main constituent) and was crucial to both reactors as well as demonstrating how it was possible to safely undertake extensive engineering work in the precincts of a highly radioactive plant. The process was similar to that of the handling of metallic fuel but with the end material being liquid plutonium-nitrate that then had to be concentrated in the plutonium evaporator plant before being shipped to Sellafield to be manufactured in to fuel units before returning to Dounreay. This transportation process was criticised at the time and, by today's standards, the specially designed flasks that were then used would not now pass the stricter regulations in force for the transport of radioactive material – although there were no accidents; so it worked. The residue was transferred to yet another building for processing and long-term storage. The highly critical safety audit of Dounreay in 1998 was instrumental in keeping this unit closed – it had been shut down earlier due to a dissolver failure in 1996.

Linked to this complex of buildings (although in the future to them) was the Dounreay cementation plant whose task was to safely immobilise intermediate level liquid waste from MTR reprocessing in preparation for its long-term storage or disposal.

Even the human servants of the dome could be (and were) self-contained within its boundaries as there was a shop, a hairdresser, medical facilities, a canteen and a dentist all on site. Highland Omnibuses expanded their services to cope with the hordes pouring in and out of the plant. Ed Adam, who was later to be so much part of PFR when that came on stream, remembers sitting on one of Highland Omnibuses' double-deckers as it slid sideways down an icy Scrabster Brae. He remembers also that you could sometimes see the road through the planking of the floor.

It was during those early years that the pioneers established themselves. There were opportunities for all. Gina MacKenzie, then a young lassie from a farming background within the county, joined in '61. She felt excited at being part of it all. Initially brought into the typing pool, she soon found herself working directly for Donald Carmichael himself – a man she has fond memories of and, like all others who knew him, described as a gentleman. Later, she was to work with site director Cliff Blumfield and then with Gerry Jordan who took over from him. She admits, as do so many, that she was in a state of trepidation at the beginning – but 41 years service suggests she got over that.

Gina Mackenzie, who was awarded an OBE for her services to the nuclear industry.

As the groundbreaking work settled into – well, never routine but with some semblance to that – so Dounreay became to be accepted as a normal part of the Caithness scene. The newly formed Dounreay Drama Group staged the play 'Look Back In Anger' as their first ever offering in that springtime of 1960. 'An adventurous choice,' opined the Caithness Courier's tactful critic.

In August that same year DFR achieved a world record for such a reactor by outputting 30 megawatts of heat. That it had taken so long was blamed mainly on the problem of gas bubbles within the 50 tonnes of liquid metal that circulated in the system – although there had been other troubles. Later that year another success was registered when DFR became the first fast reactor to feed electricity into the national grid on a commercial basis – it may only have been a trickle at a mere 2 megawatt but it was a fine accomplishment nonetheless. Dr. Hurst stated at the time, 'One of the outstanding and most gratifying features of the Dounreay project has been the whole-hearted support which from the very outset it has received from the local authorities in Caithness.'

With equal truth he could also have added 'and from the local people as well.' All this led Mr. John L. Russell, the County Clerk, to declare that, 'Caithness was on the crest of a wave.'

And yet, as DFR and the individuals concerned with it were receiving justified praise, thoughts had already turned to the next stage. Before a truly meaningful reactor producing electricity on an industrial scale could be built a large working model of such a commercial reactor was required – a prototype or, as the industry named it, a PFR (prototype fast reactor).

And whilst this was being discussed, Mrs. E. Doris of Droitwich (in 1963) became the 15,000th visitor at the Visitor Centre, which had been set up in the air traffic control tower, and had her picture taken with a fully kilted William Sinclair, the exhibition guide. Willie, a Caithness native, was highly articulate and used a model of the site to explain to visitors the role of Dounreay; there were no glossy brochures, video presentations nor even working models back then. Indeed, giving out written information about the site could well have been construed as a breach of security.

DFR achieved its maximum electrical output of 15 megawatts in July 1963.

That its output figures were seriously considered and measured had been demonstrated at an earlier celebration when the reactor first made ten megawatts. The celebratory gathering was interrupted by a concerned operator who announced that a re-evaluation of the power output showed

LOCATING PFR

Winfrith in Dorset, another UKAEA research centre, was considered to be the favoured site for construction of the prototype fast reactor. Frank Cousins, the Minister for Technology, wanted research concentrated on a single site and believed the remote location would send out wrong messages about safety if it were chosen again. It was also estimated to be £8 million cheaper in the south than the north.

But the Scottish Secretary, Willie Ross, did not concede. In a strongly worded memorandum, he underlined the consequences that would face the new Highlands and Islands Development Board when DFR closed with the potential loss of some 1200 jobs; £7.5 million of public money had been invested in new schools and housing around Dounreay, and £2 million would be required to find alternative work to sustain this. Community leaders also fought Dounreay's case. For the Highlands and Islands Development Board, which pressed hard to establish the region as the recognised world leader in the practical development of fast reactor technology, the decision was a test of the Government's commitment to regeneration of the Highlands and Islands.

Sir John Hill, a former chairman of UKAEA, later recalled: "The battle was fiercely fought. The Secretary of State for Scotland said he would resign if the fast reactor did not go to Scotland. At the same Cabinet meeting was a paper from the Navy asking for a new aircraft carrier and the Minister for the Navy said he would resign if the Navy did not get its new ship, the most vital requirement. The Cabinet decided it could afford to lose one Minister but not two. The Secretary of State for Scotland was the least expensive so PFR went to Dounreay and the Minister for the Navy resigned."

Frank Cousins made the announcement on the "system of the next century" on February 9, 1966. "They will be able to produce new nuclear fuel in the course of their operation and offer a prospect of even greater economy, as well as conservation in the use of uranium," he said.

UKAEA chairman Sir William Penney declared the target was to have commercial fast reactor power stations by 1978, though he conceded UKAEA would have a "real tough time" meeting this timescale. Construction would create 700 jobs in Caithness.

only 9.9 megawatts. This figure was within the range of the tolerance of the instruments but, although the party continued, the next day the reactor was run at a full 10.5 megawatts simply to make certain.

During the entire lifetime of DFR the reactor itself performed smoothly; all of the problems concerned either the coolant or the heat exchangers. Some of these related to inadequate design; the heat rejection plant that consisted of twelve units, leaked extensively. Much stress corrosion cracking was found and when the water in the superheater headers was analysed, instead of 0.1 parts per million (ppm) of chloride in it there was almost 38. Moisture had got into the tubes from the sea air. Once the tubes were replaced the problem was solved.

Another problem was completely unexpected. Early in 1965 some of the natural uranium breeder elements in the surrounding outer blanket of the reactor were found to be swollen; to such an extent were they so that special tools and equipment had to be designed and made to extricate them. This surprised as, although they had been working for six years, they had burnt up only less than half a percent of their capacity. Yet 200 elements were jammed. To get them out small sections of the tube had to be cut away.

Analysis revealed that these elements had been heated above the anticipated temperature and this had been caused by fluctuations in the flow of the coolant. Today we know that with such high temperatures blips in the circulation of coolant can be expected. The answer back then was to increase the pumping power to ensure a more even flow of coolant. Yet even this problem proved a positive in that it displayed a potential hazard that had to be accounted for in any future reactor.

And, about this time in 1966, the good news broke that the future reactor, the PFR, was coming to Dounreay. Despite its experience, despite its expertise and despite the support of the local community, Dounreay had never been favourite – but not always do favourites win. Although PFR was not expected to increase employment the expected £28 million investment would maintain job levels. Caithness was, indeed, on the crest of a wave.

Even a little leak when it happened, such a little leak, did not upset things because the Magnificent Seven and 350 other guys were around.

PERSONNEL

Initially there was no separate function of a personnel department; personnel matters were dealt with as part of the site administration. The head of Administration was of senior staff status, a position almost akin to director level. The first individual appointed to this post was Kenneth W. Matthews who, like so many, quickly settled in the area even down to acquiring a small croft in Sutherland along where, as a part-time activity, he helped rear sheep and cattle.

When Personnel was formed as a separate function it was organised into three sections, Personnel, Labour and Welfare. Personnel had the primary role of selection and recruitment of staff – a massive task, particularly in the early years – and, thereafter, were responsible for the career development of the staff. The Labour section dealt with work matters pertaining to the individual, e.g. complaint procedures, disciplinary matters, etc. The Welfare section handled personal problems affecting members of staff and their families such as illness, bereavement and family problems in general.

With the changes that overtook the site following the Parkinson announcement in 1988, Personnel was reduced in numbers with the Labour section integrating into Personnel and Welfare eventually being operated on a part-time basis.

Today, Personnel has morphed into the Human Resources Department, a title that, perhaps, better reflects the importance of the human input into Dounreay.

Chapter Seventeen
The Magnificent Seven

It was May '67 when a detector set inside the leak jacket surrounding the primary coolant system (the one that ran through the reactor and hence was radioactive) registered the presence of NaK – where, of course, there should not have been any.

The dry official report talks of normal shutdown procedures being applied; it was a little harder than that. Shutting down on sparse evidence of what appeared a very negligible leak was not a light-hearted decision. But radiation was involved so there was no option; the concern was that there might be a breach of containment.

Shortly after shutdown, as always appears to happen in such matters, the leak appeared to stop – and this with the system pressurised: falling back on old civil service procedures a committee was formed, the aptly titled Dounreay Leak Investigation Executive. It was decided to continue with the planned refuelling but adding further detection instrumentation before, cautiously, restarting.

The reactor ran a further three weeks and the leak rate – incredibly slow but still measurable – was increasing. Again the reactor was stopped but this time the decision was taken to keep it stopped until the leak had been located and repaired.

By this time a relationship had been established between the reactor power and the leak, a circumstance that suggested the leak was widening under thermal stress. The whole of the vessel and the pipe work were then subjected to gas leakage tests that established that the leak was either at one of the twenty-four outlet nozzles, or in one of the twenty-four outlet pipes. Pressurizing the leak jacket and listening for bubbling noises failed to narrow the options. The crack causing the leak, estimated at around one-fifteen thousandths of an inch in diameter, would have to be opened up to increase the leak in order to find it.

The coolant was removed as well as the active fuel elements. A more precise location was obtained when the vessel was filled with eutectic

An engineer surveying the wooden model of the reactor.

NaK and microphones were clamped in position. The leak was sourced to within a short distance from the outlet of the reactor (a defective stub in circuit 10A) and a circumferential weld was suspected.

A full-scale model of the reactor and its associated pipe work was constructed out of wood in order both to devise a method of dealing with the leak and to permit operators to practise the exact tasks they would have to undertake when once within the biological shield.

Such a trial run was not unique in Dounreay's history. Earlier in the same year a special cage had been constructed with 4 inch thick lead walls to permit two operators to enter the blanket cave of the fuel element reprocessing plant to repair a faulty crack; the 'cave' was a 40 foot high building used to store the highly active fuel element rods after they had been in the core of the reactor. The operators in the cage wore lead gloves and aprons and a 'frog' suit which had a breathing tube attached to allow them air from the outside. A lifeline was also affixed to enable the operator to be hauled out at a moment's notice. Much the same type of suit would be used by operators to mend the leak.

This type of suiting is cumbrous and warm to work in but it was the high levels of radiation that limited each operator to only a few minutes of work. A worker had to know exactly what to do before entering the radiation zone, working within a few short feet of the reactor (now with its fuel removed), and each had to be closely monitored as they did so – which was the task of the supervisors assigned to the project. Since these supervisors numbered seven it was inevitable that they became known as the 'Magnificent Seven' after the famous Hollywood film of 1960 featuring Yul Bryner. Although the operators were not facing wild banditos as Yul was, nevertheless, because of the radiation doses they were receiving, once they had carried out their specific task, they were not permitted to work there again – most received in a day what was then considered the three-month radiation limit. Thus over 350 operators had to be drafted in, each to do a bit.

To make the repair a three-yard section of the suspected pipe was cut out and a thin crack found in the weld. The weld had failed because of several defects. The main problem was that there had been a slight misalignment of the pipes and the weld bead had strayed. It had also come under thermal stress in this region because of the close proximity of a smaller bore return pipe from the circuit's by-pass system that introduced relatively cooler NaK into the hotter main circuit stream.

Six of the other twenty-three coolant circuit stubs had similar NaK returns from their by-pass circuits at precisely the same point and it was consequently decided that these circuits also would best be modified. This decision increased the repair work six-fold.

It took until June of the following year before the reactor returned to full power. The supervisors acquired most of their lifetime's dose of radiation at that time. Since then their health has been closely monitored and all have shown no ill effects as a result. None of the 350 men involved in the entire operation would want to be called heroes but how many people would want to willingly go alongside a leaking nuclear reactor. As Ed Adam said, 'They all knew the issues involved – '

The whole operation, stemming from a failure, was turned into a constructive part of the learning process. It had been demonstrated that even an incredibly difficult leak could be traced and stopped and a fault in the design had been exposed. Ed Adam went onto PFR and ended as station manager when PFR finally closed.

FLYING HIGH

The inaugural flight took place on 6 April 1970.

Regular flights began to use the airfield at Dounreay in 1970 to meet the transportation needs of the civil site and neighbouring Vulcan facility. For 20 years until 1990, when the airport at Wick was upgraded and the site agreed to reroute its traffic there, Dounreay was an operational airfield.

The inaugural operator was Northern Air Taxis of Leeds, which flew to Manchester for links to the UKAEA design office at nearby Risley and then to London where the UKAEA had its headquarters for 40 years. When VernAir won the contract, it used Liverpool and replaced the Beagle 206 aircraft with a 10/13-seater Beechcraft Queenair, later followed by Kingair turboprops. The final contractor was Northern Executive Aviation, which resorted to Manchester.

Other regular users of the airstrip included the Northern Lighthouse Board, which refuelled its helicopters being used to change crews at remote lighthouses around the north of Scotland.

MEDICAL MATTERS

Jill Nicholson.

The medical amenities at Dounreay back up and support the emergency services as well as providing ongoing health checks on all employees. Jill Nicholson has been at the site since 1994. Born and bred a Wicker she was, nevertheless, brought up in Dunfermline where her parents had moved when Jill was four. She was trained in nursing in Edinburgh and worked in local hospitals specialising in cardiac care as well as general nursing.

But the strings of Caithness are unbreakable. She moved back in 1993 and took up a post as occupational health specialist with the Authority. Like so many she found Dounreay daunting to begin with – particularly in relation to the security environment. However she quickly settled appreciating her colleagues and the friendly and professional atmosphere. The aim of the medical department is to keep people at work by keeping them healthy and to this end it is extremely well provided for – a mini-hospital in fact well able to cater for everything from a stubbed toe to a heart attack. All importantly, any patient who has been contaminated with radioactive material can be treated in the isolation area. A doctor visits and holds a surgery on a daily basis. There are eight full time staff employed; five nurses, a physiotherapist, an administrative assistant and the departmental manager who is also a nurse.

Despite being in an environment with which radiation and radioactivity are necessarily linked, the greatest concern has been a meningitis outbreak of recent vintage connected to the PFR plant. Fortunately there were no fatalities but it proved a stressful time for all – but it was a test that the department coped with and under-scored the professionalism required in such a place as Dounreay.

Chapter Eighteen
PFR

PFR viewed from the meadow.

The prototype fast reactor (PFR) came directly off the back of DFR. DFR had demonstrated, and demonstrated effectively, that a fast reactor could be operated reliably and safely to produce electricity and that the use of liquid metal coolant was feasible. PFR was to replicate a full-scale industrial reactor capable of producing meaningful quantities of electricity taking into account the lessons learnt from DFR.

PFR was to use pins (not rods) as fuel, each some 9 feet long but only 5.8 mm in diameter with a thin stainless steel wrap around them. 325 pins made up a hexagonal prism and 78 of these were surrounded by bundles of 58 breeder fuel assemblies in a honeycomb pattern.

The whole centre of the reactor was contained in an enormous stainless steel tank 50 foot deep and 120 feet in circumference. This tank contained the reactor core, the breeder area, the inner shielding, three pumps for circulating the primary coolant and six heat exchangers. From the first however the project suffered from various delays.

There was a fear at the time (unjustified in hindsight) that as nuclear power spread a world shortage of uranium would occur, therefore the PFR had to maximise the uranium that it used (the Dounreay plutonium fuel plant came on stream during 1970). The design of an appropriate fuel element with an adequate burn up therefore proved to be the first delay, as did the discovery of neutron induced swelling of the steel in DFR. Late modifications to the core design also held back progress.

Added to these niggling matters there was a series of strikes and go slows at the Dalmuir Works in Clydebank (there was also industrial turbulence at

Dounreay as well), where the primary tank roof was being manufactured. Dalmuir Works had announced it was closing down and this led to problems as low morale there took its toll. The roof finally arrived two years late and took another year to complete on-site.

Shut down of DMTR by Peter Mummery.

And whilst this was all happening a rather sad ceremony was being carried out by Peter Mummery, the site director, as he pressed the button that closed down DMTR in May of 1969. There were complaints about the quiet and unceremonial closure as DMTR slipped into history. However, it was probably the best way. DFR and one of the Authority's other reactors at Harwell would fill the gap. It says something of the increasing concerns surrounding Dounreay at the time that, shortly after DMTR was closed a 'Dounreay Vigilance Committee' was inaugurated to combat any run down at the complex.

In addition to the various delays on PFR (annually, from 1970 onwards, the The John O'Groat Journal predicted that PFR would commence the following year) some design mistakes were to reveal themselves as the reactor finally started. The reactor itself, as with DFR, was exempt from criticism. The problems related mainly to welding flaws – and mainly to a critical weld between the tube and tube plate of the steam generators. This had been identified as a potential problem before construction but no effective solution had been implemented and the failure of welds bedevilled the operation for years.

The steam plant moreover, was to prove inflexible in action with a noticeable lack of both alternative stand-by systems and isolation valves to facilitate maintenance and by-pass requirements. Many of the main components had been designed and manufactured on a first time basis without prior experience of their performance and reliability. They were, in effect, prototypes within a prototype and the operation of the reactor, once it did get underway, exposed a number of flaws – this was particularly true regarding the fuel element handling systems, the primary and secondary heat exchangers and the pumping arrangements.

Nevertheless, three years late, on the 2nd of March 1974, PFR began running on low power.

There were a number of crucial differences in PFR to its predecessor. Unlike DFR and its famous dome, PFR sat beneath ground level in a huge but largely anonymous rectangular building adjacent to the dome. Confidence had been gained from running DFR and fears of a major incident were non-existent despite PFR's capability to produce 600 megawatts of heat (250 megawatts of electricity) against DFR's more modest 60 megawatts (about 15 megawatts

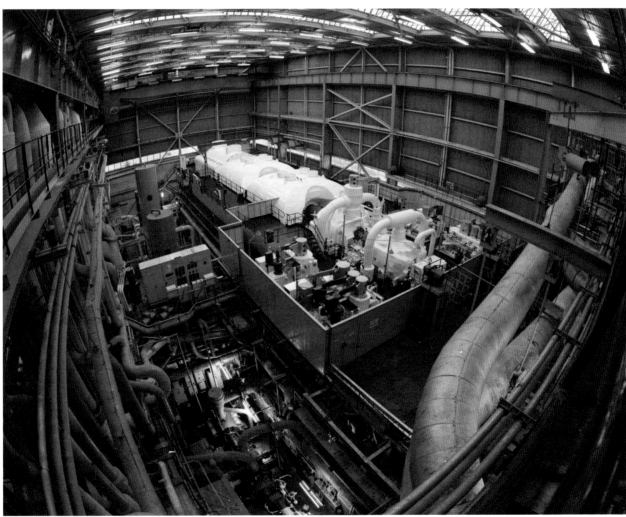

The 250 megawatt turbine.

View showing the complexities of the PFR reactor core tank.

Other lessons were also applied. The coolant in PFR (1,000 tons to the 60 tons of DFR) was to be sodium. This obviated the difficulties experienced in handling a potassium-sodium compound (and sodium alone was cheaper). The word 'coolant' is a relative term since it was between 400°C to 430°C before it entered the core. The flow of this sodium was upwards through the core and not downwards as it was in DFR. This eliminated the tendency to trap gas bubbles in the flow.

The fuel used was plutonium-uranium oxide sealed in stainless steel clad pins (not rods) and this increased the burn up rate and helped prevent contamination of the coolant. The pumps employed this time would not be electro-magnetic but higher capacity (and smaller) centrifugal ones and the steam generator was of an advanced tube-in-shell design.

Advanced design perhaps, but the first ten operating years were wracked by failures of the tube-to-tube plate welds and the highest load factor achieved was only 12%. After the problems were overcome, plant performance improved and the final year of operation saw a 56% figure achieved.

of electricity). It was considered that with ceramic fuel being used and extremely sensitive and advanced instrumentation in place any serious incident would be prevented – and that shutdown would be rapid if required.

Before that a lot had happened including an incident, not greatly remarked at the time, which was to become highly controversial later. In 1977 there was an explosion.

THE FLOWERS REPORT

The first serious jolt to Britain's fast reactor programme came from an unexpected source in 1976. It came in the conclusions of a report called Nuclear Power and the Environment, based on evidence given to the Royal Commission on Environmental Pollution chaired by Sir Brian Flowers.

This was a time when the first public concerns about the safety of nuclear energy and its environmental impact were surfacing and a number of anti-nuclear campaigners were also involved in submitting evidence to the Commission.

With the UK looking to bring the fast reactor into widespread commercial use, the Commission said: "Our concern is that the UK planning might depend too much on the introduction of fast breeder reactors on a substantial scale and move into a plutonium economy."

The report found that "too little effort had been devoted to problems of long-term management" of the radioactive waste generated by nuclear energy and there should be no substantial expansion until a method of safe disposal of the waste had been established beyond reasonable doubt.

The Department of Energy and UKAEA both presented forecasts of UK energy needs that, with the benefit of hindsight, proved unrealistically high. Britain was expected to need three times as much electricity by 2000 as it in reality required and 33 fast reactors were envisaged as being in service by the start of the 21st century.

The Flowers Report also identified the widespread use of plutonium as a security issue that required public debate and pointed to the possibility of its illicit use in the manufacture of terrorist weapons.

Chapter Nineteen
Explosion

Lord Hinton shutting down DFR.

1977 was to prove a seminal year for Dounreay.

DFR closed down.

What Dounreay had been all about was gone. The decision to close DFR had been taken as far back as 1973. Despite its problems, perhaps because of the problems it revealed, DFR had been a success. It richly

deserved its being featured in a special stamp in 1964 produced for the Twentieth International Geographical Congress. The reactor had been the first of its type and was built without any precedent to follow. The multi-layered facets of handling such a reactor and its associated coolant system had become known and this had provided a library of valuable data and information. Theory had been checked against actual performance and much had been discovered - particularly concerning the phenomenon of void swelling and the performance of fuels. In its latter years it had largely taken over from DMTR as a means of studying the behaviour of materials subjected to irradiation. In this role it had earned money as overseas customers paid for the privilege of carrying out their own experiments with it. The first such contract had been for £750,000 and, in 1971, it brought in well over £1 million.

Appropriately it was Christopher Hinton (now Lord Hinton) who, in a short ceremony, began the run down sequence. He made no bones about why Dounreay had been chosen all those years ago. 'It was not known whether fast reactors would be as controllable as thermal reactors. If there was a failure in the coolant supply, the fuel might melt and form a critical mass. It was therefore decided to build on a remote site.'

The decommissioning itself was no easy task. Pipelines were blocked by NaK and damaged and jammed breeder elements remained stubbornly stuck in the outer blanket. Even the reduced capacity of the water filled pond for

Diagram showing the shaft and the tunnel.

The devastation around the shaft following the explosion.

storage of radioactive waste proved a hindrance. Although most of the core was removed lack of effective storage space at the time as well as the condition of parts of the breeder blanket led to much being deferred.

Work still continues on the clean up to this day.

PFR was still struggling with leaks although, early in the year, it achieved a notable output of 600 megawatts of heat. Even that was a triumph manqué because its output to the grid was only 200 megawatts due to failure in the generation equipment.

However, the main event of that year was, perchance, not immediately recognised as such. The blast occurred in the 213-foot deep waste shaft (in current Dounreay literature now referred to as the 65-metre shaft) at twenty past midnight on the 10th of May.

It resonated throughout the site as, later, it was to resonate through the media. A security officer at HMS Vulcan reported observing a large white cloud coming from Dounreay and heading seaward. But it was an hour later before a Dounreay officer, on patrol, discovered glass and concrete strewn around the shaft's opening. The fourteen foot thick concrete cap (almost five tons in weight) that had topped the shaft lay some feet away. Debris was scattered around a radius of 100 feet – pieces of equipment were found beyond the security fence that had been damaged in the vicinity of the explosion. A tangle of rubble lay strewn around, including the remnants of scaffolding that had fallen into the shaft.

Immediate checks in the vicinity showed no detectable radioactivity (although a later log entry talks of 10 to 20 millisieverts an hour) but some contamination was found on equipage near the shaft. This was swiftly cleared up and further examination revealed that no large quantities of radioactivity had been dispersed.

The shaft had first been drilled in 1956 to act as an entry point to the 2,000-foot long tunnel leading out under the sea from the pump house. Its main purpose had been as an egress for spoils from the tunnel digging. After completion of the main tunnel a massive plug of steel and concrete had sealed the tunnel from the shaft. In 1957 permission had been sought and granted from the Scottish Office (against the advice of its own geologists) to recognise the shaft as a waste depository for contaminated radioactive material (permission would not have been granted today under the stricter regulations now applying). For the most part the sides of the shaft, cutting through the fractured sandstone, remained bare and unlined. Over the period it had acted as a receptacle for some 11,000 dumping transactions (later, there were to be allegations of unrecorded tippings as well).

The explosion itself was a conventional one, not involving nuclear materials, and was estimated at the (surprisingly small) equivalent of three pounds of TNT from the position of the concrete plug that had been on top of the shaft. At an immediate inquiry afterwards it was explained that DFR components had been placed in the shaft prior to the explosion and that these may have been contaminated with NaK. ('The cleaning of NaK contaminated waste may not always have been entirely effective' admitted a spokesman for Dounreay). Exposure of this to water could have caused a chemical reaction in which hydrogen would have been released. The volatility of the NaK itself may then have led to the ignition of the hydrogen although it may also have been the workings of the pumps that were used to keep the water level in the shaft down. Later, it was to be claimed that raw NaK had also been poured down the shaft in 1977 (2 kilos worth, to be exact).

It was swiftly determined at the time though that the shaft walls had not been damaged and that the bottom plug was in good condition. There was a back filling put in on the sea side of this plug to provide extra protection for the future (the Authority have never denied the possibility of an other explosion – although consider it extremely unlikely). The area around the top of the shaft was cleaned up and the shaft closed again and a fence placed around it. UKAEA operator's searched for any coastal contamination (erroneously described later as 'secret' searches).

The hydrogen in the shaft had not only set off an explosion but also a great swirl of activity as Dounreay came to terms with the fact that all was not well and that mistakes had been made. One of the worst was that not everything that had been disposed of into the shaft had been properly listed. This was later blamed on dumping during the 'silent hours' as evening and night operations were known. Another mistake was the Authority's reticence in telling the world about the accident – not from the point of view of trying to hide anything but simply because it was not then their way to talk of things. It was noted in the media at the time and the matter was raised in Parliament though so it was not kept hidden. Later commentators were to refer to the 'excessive secrecy' that characterised UKAEA operations at the time and, many years later in the Nineties, the Glasgow Herald (now the Herald) was to state, 'The disposal of the radioactive waste at Dounreay has been a disgrace. What is more, it has been a secret disgrace, hidden from the public and characterised by the obsessive secrecy and intolerant arrogance which has marked so much of Dounreay's interaction with anyone who failed to share their nuclear goal.'

All strong stuff and deserved in so far as Dounreay had retreated into itself long since. The openness of the early days, encouraged by Christopher Hinton, had gone. Criticisms about nuclear power and the nuclear programme were mounting and various accidents at nuclear plants around the world had encouraged that.

Equally, the civil nuclear programme had become entangled with the use of nuclear power for military ends and emotions, in certain quarters, ran high.

Chapter Twenty
Particles

1978 saw Clifford Blumfield, director of Dounreay, embroiled in more defence of the plant as criticisms (some justified, some quite wild) mounted. However, in a re-run from a more hopeful period, the Authority held another open day – this time for the families of employees who were given conducted tours of the reactor and its associated fuel processing and fuel technology areas including the main engineering workshop. Again it was a success and, on the back of this, organised tours were then started around the plant for tourists – the tourists were even taken onto the top of the reactor. At the same time Allison Dyer, one of the first of the 'atomic babies' became also the first to graduate (at Edinburgh University).

Early next year, striking a sourer note, the Labour Minister, Tony Benn, opined of Dounreay that it was, 'A billion pound step down a technological path which may later prove unacceptable or even catastrophic.' The Royal Commission on Environmental Pollution tended to support this view although their views were nowhere near as extreme. Later the highly articulate Benn would also state, 'There has grown up a powerful lobby of scientists and vested interests who are determined that nothing will come to light that throws doubt on the safety of nuclear power – civilian nuclear power is the public front for nuclear weapons.'

Thus it was an era of increasing concern about the effects of nuclear power. However, Dounreay still remained positive. Increasingly there was talk of building a commercial fast reactor – a reactor that would produce electricity on an industrial scale. The case for this was strengthened in 1984 when, at last, PFR hit high output rates (the steam generator had been repaired) and began putting some meaningful amounts of power down the new high voltage lines that had been laid in anticipation of this moment. The lines ran all the way to Beauly (just north of Inverness) where they joined with the rest of the national grid. Shortly after, into 1985, PFR achieved its maximum of 250 MW of electricity and exceeded a 20% burn-up of its fuel.

Monitoring the foreshore for particles began during the 80s.

The same year witnessed the report of a survey on the incidence of childhood leukaemia in Caithness and this showed well above average figures. Fragments of radioactive spent fuel had already been discovered on the beach in front of Dounreay in 1983 and surveys in early 1984 discovered radioactive contamination on a beach used by the public at Sandside. Dounreay was immediately suspected as the cause of the leukaemia outbreak and it came increasingly under attack from various groups. Clifford Blumfield's statement that Dounreay had exuded less than one-tenth the radiation that could have been expected from a conventional power plant went largely unreported compared to his admission that low radiation particles had indeed turned up on the local beach. Further to this, the fuel reprocessing plant (the EDRP) that had been urged by Dounreay as a new addition to the site was condemned in a public meeting in Wick.

The finding of radioactive particles on the beaches and foreshore around Dounreay continued (and continues) to be a problem. It was only in 1997 that it was revealed that some scientists had openly advocated a release of waste onto the foreshore – this prior to Dounreay being operational. Christopher Hinton had denounced their thinking at the time as 'light-hearted.' Others would have had stronger words. Hinton said, 'I have read the résumé of the discussion on the "Proposed experiments in connection with the discharge into the sea at Dounreay" and should like to make it clear that I am in absolute disagreement with the approach which is being adopted by the discussion group'.

But the foreshore had been contaminated anyway. In 1997 fishing in the area was banned.

Over the years there has been controversy over the finds of radioactive particles on the beaches and sea rocks around Dounreay. COMARE, the Government committee of experts that investigated the leukaemia cluster, says of the particles, ' – if encountered they present a real hazard to health

Pylons linking PFR to the national grid.

A particle being analysed in a Dounreay laboratory.

When it came to reprocessing these fuel rods the end pieces were milled off to lessen the amount of aluminium that would be involved. Although in the beginning the milling was carried out under controlled conditions and the swarf placed in specially designed ponds eventually it was undertaken remotely under the shielding water of the ponds. Every so often, the swarf generated required cleaning out. Most of this was scooped up and disposed to the shaft but, over time, unknown quantities were carried out by the draining water into the sites effluent drainage system.

Although this system was designed to cope with radioactive matter by having two discharge tanks where particulate matter could settle and thus avoid being discharged to sea, not all the swarf did so. Agitation of the water prior to discharge for sampling purposes inevitably meant that some of the fragments were carried out to sea.

There were other incidents as well. In the early 1970s, fuel from the reactor that had not been allowed to cool for very long caught fire in a reprocessing plant and this also led to particulate in the radioactive effluent reaching the effluent drains.

and the hottest particles could induce serious acute radiation effects – while the probability of encountering a particle is small, it is not negligible, if individuals ingested particles with radioactivity levels at the top of the range, fatalities might occur.' COMARE also made it clear that they did not consider the particles as the source of the leukaemia cluster in Caithness.

Today Dounreay acknowledges that it may never be known for certain how all the particles escaped into the environment. Whilst nothing can be proven absolutely one main route taken by the particles to the sea and then back to land again has been worked out. It is tortuous but credible.

In the 60s, when DMTR was operating, some of the fuel used for that reactor was a hard metallic alloy of aluminium and uranium lying like the meat in a sandwich between two slices of bread – the bread being in this case thin sheetings of aluminium. These long plates were sealed at the top and along the sides and assembled into fuel units.

Divers have discovered a plume or fan pattern of particles (they can be dated to when DMTR was operating) spraying out from the discharge. Every now and again the chamber at the discharge would become blocked with silt and a high-pressure blast would be used to clear it thus spreading anything in the chamber out.

It has been speculated that the particles may have come from the infamous shaft since it is known such particles reside there. That this may have been the case can never quite be ruled out, as while it is always possible (if only theoretically) that odd extremely fine particles could permeate through the twisted labyrinthine route of the fine cracks in the rock detailed investigations and groundwater modelling have shown this to be extremely unlikely. The British Geological Survey have analysed samples taken at points where fresh water seeps out of the rocks but no radioactive particles have ever been found.

EXTRACT

from its "Second Report", Committee on Medical Aspects of Radiation in the Environment, 1988:

Six cases of leukaemia were registered amongst young people aged 0-24 resident within 25km of Dounreay during the period 1968-1984. This is twice the number expected on the basis of the national rate. Five of the cases were resident within 12.5km of Dounreay, this is three times the number expected in the period.

The most striking feature of the results is the concentration of the cases in the last six years of the period studied 1979-1984. All six cases resident within 25km of Dounreay were registered in this period whereas approximately one case would have been expected. This number of cases would occur by chance only very infrequently.

There is evidence of a raised incidence of leukaemia among young people living in the vicinity of Dounreay. There are differences between Dounreay and Sellafield, principally a difference of one or more orders of magnitude in discharge levels. However, the evidence of a raised incidence of leukaemia near Dounreay, taken in conjunction with that relating to the area around Sellafield, tends to support the hypothesis that some feature of the nuclear plants that we have examined leads to an increased risk of leukaemia in young people living in the vicinity of those plants. Conventional dose and risk estimates suggest that neither authorised nor accidental discharges could be responsible. There are however uncertainties about dose and risk calculations, especially with respect to exposure of the foetus and small child, high LET emissions and prolonged low-level exposure.

The Committee have considered a number of alternative explanations, including other mechanisms by which the authorised discharges could be implicated; the possibility that parental occupational exposure could be relevant; and the possibility that factors other than radiation could be important. However, in the Committee's view the evidence does not point to any particular explanation, and therefore all possible explanations need to be investigated further. Although chance cannot be entirely dismissed as an explanation of the raised incidence of childhood leukaemia in the vicinity of Dounreay, we consider that it is now less likely than when Sellafield was considered in isolation."

Shortly after the first clutch of particles was found filters were installed on the ponds and the groundwater being pumped from the shaft was filtered as well. Dounreay's public relations handling of the problem backfired when COMARE found that their official explanation at the time did not stack up. Sir John Knill, from the Radioactive Waste Management Advisory Committee of COMARE stated, in 1995, 'To say they (the UKAEA) were lying is not an unreasonable conclusion to come to.'

Dounreay had stated that the particles had emanated from a back siphon of water from a fuel pond in 1965 that had been washed down a storm drain – yet the investigators discovered that one of the particles found on the foreshore was, in itself, more radioactive than the entire spillage in 1965. COMARE complained of discovering the truth by accident. And when they learned that the 1977 explosion had been suspected as a cause of the particles but that fact was not communicated to the team investigating the leukaemia cluster, they complained loudly and publicly.

COMARE also concluded in their report that it was unlikely that the particles being found could have accounted for the high incidence of leukaemia cases in the area (a similar leukaemia cluster has been found at Sellafield). Of late some suspicion has fallen onto the incidence of pylons carrying high-energy power lines as a recent study (June, 2005) has related the prevalence of childhood leukaemia to the proximity of such pylons. The increased risk is small and as yet not proven absolutely but if it is so then Dounreay would then be less directly implicated in the incidence of childhood leukaemia and the whole issue of how power is moved around would have to be considered. A more specific source to Caithness has also been suggested in the microwave signals that the United States Navy station at Forss were using – again no definite proof.

Another speculation is that the incidence of leukaemia is linked to the influx of new people into the remote and rural area. Similar circumstances elsewhere have also produced outbreaks.

However, there is no final evidence for any cause. Today, all the suspected area around Dounreay is regularly monitored for particles.

Nukem Ltd carrying out reassurance monitoring on a local beach.

REPORT ON LEUKAEMIA CLUSTER FROM DOUNREAY

"It is a fact that the incidence of childhood leukaemia is raised in an area 10km east of Dounreay," wrote Dr Roy Nelson, the director of Dounreay, in 1997 in his report Dounreay, Past, Present and Future. "Naturally, this has been attributed by some to the activities of Dounreay.

Despite extensive investigation by the Government's appointed Committee on Medical Aspects of Radiation in the Environment, no causal link has been found. COMARE considers the radiation levels from Dounreay discharges to be at least a thousand times too small to be a factor. It considers radioactive particles from Dounreay to be an unlikely cause. Children who have contracted leukaemia do not have raised levels of radioactivity in their bodies. There is no established link to gene damage in parents; nor have any other parental employment factors been found.

"The investigations have been intensive and it now seems likely that the cluster will be attributed to a combination of relative affluence, an inwards rapid population migration and some kind of process based upon infection."

COMMUNICATING

One benefit from all the criticism being levelled at Dounreay at the time particles were being found was the development of a professional public relations department. Something like that had existed from the beginning and Hinton had led by example in being willing to talk of what was happening at Dounreay but the first formal communications were strictly internal and carried out by administrative staff. This was the cold war era and the UKAEA, being subjected to the Official Secrets Act, had to carefully guard much of what it was up to; there were admonitory signs all along the main road opposite the site warning that photography was strictly forbidden. Press releases by UKAEA were few and far between and then generally only issued upon the visit of prominent people. It was Clifford Blumfield who largely changed this and encouraged a more open approach. He recognised that there was a benefit in explaining what Dounreay was about and what it was doing. He appointed a 'Visits Liaison Officer' and had a public relations manager brought in.

Increasingly, from that time onwards, there was a growing awareness of the need to keep the public properly informed as to what was happening. There was even a spell when a Dounreay News TV programme was played into staff rooms and canteens at lunchtime. That ceased (it was costly) but tours of the site were initiated and organised site visits encouraged after the success of the second open day in 1978. Some 7,000 tourists per annum were shown around the plant from then until late 1993.

Today, broadcasting what is going on is encouraged at Dounreay and a long series of pamphlets and brochures have been produced telling of the various functions of buildings and facilities on-site. There is a highly professional and sophisticated department dealing solely in communications and charged with telling the world what is going on and, in response to wilder press stories, to tell the world what is not. There are still some restrictions put on news though (largely due to the increasing activities of world-wide terror groups) but the culture is now one of involving the public as much as possible and explaining as much as possible what is happening – which includes telling all that is known with regard to the particle finds.

Chapter Twenty-One
Modern Times

Construction of the PFR seaweed barrier.

The Eighties were not a good time for the Authority with an increasing number of radioactive particles being found and with it facing rising criticisms – and not only from anti-nuclear organisations.

Despite this, Dounreay remained positive. A cementation plant for the solidification of liquid waste was installed in 1984 in order to improve both the storage and control of such refuse and to cement the accumulation of the years from 1958 onwards. Outline planning permission for a reprocessing plant was approved the following year; and 1985 was also the first year that PFR had the luxury of running with a full set of steam generating units. And then there was the exciting prospect of European collaboration on a fast reactor with Dounreay playing a key role in reprocessing the fuel.

The plans for this, the reprocessing of fuel, were, however, to prove highly controversial   even with Caithness folk who, on the whole, were still very supportive of Dounreay. Sir Walter Marshall, the chairman of the Central Electricity Board, was still thoroughly upbeat though when he opened the research laboratory that was to be named after him. He talked enthusiastically of future funding for the fast reactor.

A detailed report and assessment on the proposed reprocessing procedures were made publicly available that year and an enquiry into it all – the 'it' now being formally titled the European Demonstration

Reprocessing Plant – began early in 1986. A collaborative agreement aimed at synergising resources on nuclear development had been signed with France, West Germany, Italy, and Belgium. It was anticipated that three new demonstration fast reactors would be constructed – one each in France, Britain and West Germany and all to a standard design.

Dounreay's part was to provide the reprocessing service for these power plants. The existing reprocessing plants in France and Britain simply did not have the capacity to cope with what was envisaged, therefore it was necessary to build and demonstrate the economics of a large-scale reprocessing plant. Dounreay was the natural site for this as it was already successfully involved in such reprocessing and there was sufficient land for expansion and the necessary infrastructure of roads, railways and airport amenities were already in place. Equally, it was considered that the majority in Caithness would welcome such a move as providing extra jobs and a more secure future.

The hearings began in Thurso on April 7th 1986; with over 1100 representations including 18 formal objections from within the county, the proceedings threatened to run a long time. The reporter was Mr. A. G. Bell and he recognised from the outset the difficulties faced by many of the interested parties at the inquiry where matters of a highly technical nature were to be discussed and where some of the participants were but lightly funded. The inquiry ran until November, setting a new record for such an event in Scotland. At the end the reporter recommended that outline planning consent be approved but subject to a number of conditions. He also recommended that no action be taken until the publication of a COMARE report into the incidence of leukaemia amongst young people in Caithness was published. By the time that came out in 1988, events elsewhere had changed circumstances anyway.

A more immediate concern to Dounreay at the time was the amount of seaweed that continued to clog the sea input end of PFR. This eventually led to a special seaweed barrier being installed (completed in '87). The total lost output due to seaweed ingression was estimated at a far from negligible 125,000MWhs.

However, the worst news for Dounreay had already broken quietly. In late 1985 the government announced it was cutting funding for fast reactor development. The local MP, Robert MacLennan – a man ever supportive of Dounreay – pressed for a statement regarding its future from Prime Minister Thatcher, but to no avail. He also sought, equally vainly, for a broadening of use of Dounreay to permit the expertise gathered there to be exploited in other, non-nuclear ways.

But, despite all the problems and the carpings of the early Eighties, the reputation of the nuclear industry still stood high – but all that changed overnight, literally overnight in the spring of 1986. The reason was summed up in one word; Chernobyl.

On the night of the 25th of April 1986, technicians at the Chernobyl nuclear plant in Ukraine attempted an experiment, shutting down one of their four reactors power regulating system and also the supporting safety systems. They then withdrew most of the control rods from the core whilst permitting the reactor to continue at a small fraction of its normal power. These errors were compounded by others and, early in the morning of the

Lord MacLennan of Rogart, formerly Robert MacLennan MP.

27th, the world's worst nuclear accident happened as the chain reaction in the core ran out of control.

NEW TROUSERS

It was at this time that a German tourist lost his trousers in the PFR plant. His slacks checked out radioactive even before he had entered: so it was off with his breeks. He had carried radioactive contamination with him from his medical work in Hamburg where he came into contact with radioactive iodine. Dounreay presented him with another pair of pants to cover his embarrassment.

THE MARSHALL LABORATORY

Walter Marshall, pictured left, opening the Marshall Laboratory. Also pictured are Dr Tom Marsham (centre) and Clifford Blumfield.

This laboratory was opened in 1986 by Walter Marshall, the head of the Central Electricity Board, and it was designed to further fast reactor research and development with particular reference to the testing and design of equipment and services thought necessary for the construction of the European Demonstration Reprocessing Plant (EDRP).

EDRP had been intended for Dounreay and the concept was that a series of new European fast reactors (each producing 1000MW) would be built in high population centres of Britain with the irradiated fuel being sent to Dounreay for reprocessing. By 1989 the European fast reactor collaboration programme had collapsed as decisions had been taken to cease such developments.

The Marshall Laboratory was where Dr. David Steele and his team developed the technique of using silver (termed the silver bullet technique) to reduce some of the most hazardous substances to harmless residue – including toxic nerve gases.

An initial steam explosion triggered a massive fireball and blew off the reactor's heavy concrete and steel lid. This released somewhere between 100 million and 200 million curies of radiation that then spewed out over northern Europe. Soviet President Mikhail Gorbachev said, ' – there has been an incredible misfortune – the accident at the Chernobyl nuclear plant has painfully affected the Soviet people and shocked the international community. For the first time, we confront the real force of nuclear energy out of control.'

The immediate significance of Chernobyl as it affected Dounreay was that it changed public attitudes. The danger inherent in nuclear power and the lurking but unspecified fears many held about such power (and it is worth noting that all power raising methods have their inherent dangers) had been given substance.

In the immediate aftermath, there was little attempt to analyse and draw weighted conclusions. More groups than ever were formed to oppose nuclear power or to oppose certain aspects of it. The proposed reprocessing plant now faced strong resistance from the North Sea Alliance – a group consisting of the Faroe Islands, Norway, Denmark and Holland.

It was at this juncture that Gerry Jordan took over as site director from Clifford Blumfield who had reached retirement. Jordan instantly walked into more problems as a major leak sprang from one of the steam generators as it operated at full power.

The dry official report states that, 'The plant protection system operated as intended.' It had. Safety valves popped open as designed and the plant automatically tripped. A failure in superheater 2 had led to a major ingression of steam into the secondary sodium circuit and the reaction that had followed led to a cascade effect of failure amongst the neighbouring tubes. The initial malfunction had been caused by a steam tube being loose enough to vibrate and, in turn, to rub against a baffle inducing fretting of the metal and leading, eventually, to the rupture. In effect it was a design fault. Whilst repairs were being undertaken and steps taken to ensure against a repetition of the incident, PFR would be out of action for over six months.

This accident was particularly irritating as the main problem over the first ten years of PFR operation – the defective welds between tube and tube-plate at the evaporators – was well on its way to being solved using a clever engineering solution whereby such suspect areas had been sleeved to by-pass them.

But it made it harder to press the case for the commercial fast reactor. Gerry Jordan made much of the fact that PFR had grossed £2 million from electricity generating. He pointed out that this was all the more remarkable given that PFR was basically involved in research and development work. And the Dounreay Action Group, an independent body of Dounreay supporters, also argued the case well for the continuance of Dounreay in an active role. They petitioned parliament, lobbied MPs, met with government officials, issued explanatory leaflets and held supportive meetings.

However, 1988 was to prove to be a defining year. Robert MacLennan called on Prime Minister Thatcher and the Secretary of State for Energy, Cecil Parkinson, to make an early statement about Dounreay to end fears that the plant could close.

Yet, the clouds gathered. After a visit to the site by John Fairclough, the chief scientific adviser to the Cabinet, Robert MacLennan came to understand that Fairclough did not support the programme of fast reactor research but the MP re-iterated his own belief that it would be commercial folly for Britain to abandon its leading role in fast reactor technology.

Despite all this, no firm statements were made by government spokespersons. The Secretary of State, Malcolm Rifkind, speaking at Wick, also followed this line. "It would be premature to say whether the Department of Energy will wish to make any recommendations at all," opined Mr. Rifkind, "the Scottish Office would be ultimately involved in any discussions."

Two weeks or so later, early in June of that year, a delegation of Highland Region and Caithness District Councillors met with Michael Spicer, the Energy Minister. He assured the delegation that the government had no intention of losing the technological initiatives gained through decades of research and development. But it all came down to cash. The economics of the fast reactor did not stack up. Uranium was no longer scarce thanks to large finds in Canada and Africa and a fast reactor was too expensive to run to be economically viable.

In July, in the House of Commons, Cecil Parkinson rose to confirm what all had been expecting, that the government would continue to fund PFR only until 1994 at latest and the reprocessing plant until 1996. Unexpected? No but it was still as if a dark blanket had been thrown over the county.

Chapter Twenty-Two
The Nineties

The immediate result of the announcement of impending rundown and ultimate closure had a galvanising effect on the county. The Caithness Chamber of Commerce called for the setting up of a Caithness Development Corporation and the Dounreay Action Group campaigned with the slogan, "Support Dounreay – It's Your Future." A wide ranging group of speakers including Labour MPs, local councillors and trade union officials came together at the Viewfirth Sports and Social Club to condemn the decision – "Grave, damaging and deeply mistaken," declared Robert MacLennan.

In terms of reversing the decision though, it all came to nought.

If the Eighties had been bad, the Nineties started well for Dounreay. The new drum-crushing machine, the supercompactor, had been installed in 1989 and was working admirably; Dounreay gaining its licence to operate from the Nuclear Installations Inspectorate of the Health and Safety Executive (NII). This was the first time the site had been licensed and was a reflection of its diversification from government research to commercial fuel work. In addition there was also still hope that the decision to end fast reactor research would be rescinded along with a widening collaboration on nuclear matters within Europe and with Japan.

Indeed, there were constructive attempts to broaden the scope of Dounreay. This had first started in the Eighties. The Department of Trade was keen that the Authority cashed in on its expertise in other areas beyond the nuclear industry. With the national move towards privatisation in the previous decade (the UKAEA had come under a trading fund arrangement in 1986), the beginning of the Nineties' witnessed the establishment of the company AEA Technology and the commercial thrust behind that saw a further nine businesses created around what had once been the monolithic

structure of the Authority. Later a tenth business was tagged on but then two were consolidated to bring the total back to nine. Three of these companies ran from Dounreay; Reactor Services, Fuel Services, and Decommissioning and Waste Management Services. Only Fuel Services (under Owen Pugh as chief executive) was headquartered at Dounreay.

The establishment of the trading fund was a rather unusual step indicating the government's wish to establish a business-like organisation without changing much of the overall structure. Under this the UKAEA was assumed to have a commercial debt of £80 million, a debt in the form of a notional loan from the National Loans Fund (the internal 'bank' for the government). This loan was deemed to have been provided on the 1st of April 1986 and the UKAEA were due to repay it over twenty years. The government decision was implemented by the Atomic Energy Act of 1986 and this act also permitted the UKAEA to borrow up to a limit of £150 million if it were deemed necessary.

Everything other than the new business set up went into a catchall organisation termed SITES – an unfortunate term that quickly morphed into Corporate Services in 1992. It all ended, appropriately, on 1st April 1994 when the position of site director was re-established and John Baxter took over as the businesses disappeared – although parts of them were to remain within the new commercial division that ultimately became AEA Technology PLC. Very rapidly RWE Nukem of Germany pounced on this new company and purchased its nuclear division. Nukem (RWE has now sold it off) now operate the contract providing health physics services to Dounreay.

But it was another leak, a bad one, that gave greatest concern to plant operators at the time (June, 1991) as, again, PFR was forced to shut down.

The staff of AEA Technology's Fuel Services Division outside its headquarters at Dounreay. From left: Colin McColm, Colin Allan, Alan Scullion, Darren Bailey, Ted Trevillion, Eileen Spearing, Elaine Forbes, John Wilkins, Brenda Chisholm, Owen Pugh, William MacDonald, Christine Bowes, Phil Cartwright, Brian Eyres (Chief Executive), Dave Thom, Carolyn Grant, Kim Sloss, Mike Imrie, Jim Frew, Eleanor Harness.

Ed Adam PFR's last station manager.

A significant quantity of oil, some 35 litres, had oozed from a pump and mingled with the sodium in the primary coolant circuit. There was concern that the oil would have left carbonaceous deposits (coke) within the system thus restricting the flow of coolant. All therefore had to be opened up and checked. "We want to prove if it's there or not there," said Ed Adam, the station manager.

Consideration was given to restarting the plant but with the Nuclear Installations Inspectorate (NII) pressing for answers, the decision was taken to remove components for inspection. It was 'Death by a thousand questions,' one of the site's senior scientists remembers of the NII's approach. So out came the pumps, the filters and the piping. PFR had been designed to permit this and the components were lifted through the top; still an extremely difficult task as many were contaminated with radioactive sodium and had to be kept within a purpose-built building, itself within the reactor hall. There were fears it would never start again but a tremendous team effort – working long hours – and the use of Russian facilities at Obminsk, where successful experiments were carried out, saved the day. Even the NII were delighted and contributed positively to the success. Although it was late in 1992, the plant did start again.

Whilst the leak was being taken care of the broader picture as to Dounreay's future still demanded attention. There was a widespread appreciation of the technical know-how of Dounreay and the high abilities of its staff and, consequently, a belief that these were assets that could be used in other ways (as Robert MacLennan had suggested); a contract from British Petroleum to clean their equipment that had become contaminated by radioactivity whilst being used in their offshore drilling platforms in the North Sea was greeted with general approval. However, the plans that were still a-brewing to reprocess waste from other sites, although it was said would secure hundreds of jobs, were highly contentious. Less controversial were the plans to use Dounreay expertise on the study and development of alternative energy strategies that would include the harnessing of energy from wind and wave power.

But the main concern was to try and raise new business. The final hope of keeping PFR going was dashed when it was confirmed that it would close early in 1994, this despite a strong case being put forward to retain it for a further three to four years. Nevertheless, some considered that reprocessing would secure the financial future and that the reprocessing plant would be the new heart of Dounreay. There was, indeed, a dramatic rise in reprocessing contracts early in '93 and the site began to make inroads into the commercial fuel market. However, smugglers had been caught offering the weapons grade fissionable material on the black market (from ex-Soviet countries) and the Americans were becoming alarmed at the flow of such material.

And other matters had gone wrong as well. A visit by local councillors to consider an extension to the low level waste pits had left those individuals

Members and officials of the Highland Regional Council inspect the low level waste pits.

SPEECH ON THE CLOSURE OF PFR

This was given by Sir John Hill, a former chairman of UKAEA at the celebratory dinner.

"You and your colleagues worldwide who are developing the fast reactor have good reason to be proud of what you have achieved. To be capable of building reactors that can produce as much electricity as we need, almost for ever, without polluting the environment with combustion products or having to import any new fuel, is some achievement. The economic environment of today does not however permit you, or any other fast nuclear team, to go ahead on a full commercial plant. It is very sad, but it is a fact. PFR has been a great success. Over the twenty years in which it has operated it has done everything that was hoped of it, and almost everything of which it was capable. It is a great pity that the Government did not give it time to complete its job, particularly as it is performing so well and covering so much of its costs from the sale of electricity. The fast reactor is the yardstick against which anything else proposed for long-term energy production will have to be measured."

decidedly unimpressed by the state of Dounreay housekeeping. 'Disgraceful,' muttered one at the condition of the low level waste pit and NIREX (another of the bewildering acronyms to emerge from the nuclear industry and standing for the Nuclear Industry Radioactive Waste Executive) commented critically on the need for 'positive practices to manage waste above ground.' The application was refused. Dounreay had let itself down in the all-important matter of housekeeping.

And, in a retrograde move, the visitor centre was closed. Only the fact that PFR finished off its final year trouble free and with record output and record takings gave some cheer – and there was even talk of using Dounreay as a centre to launch satellites. In fact, there was a feasibility study undertaken on the subject. The satellites would have orbited from Pole to Pole rather than around the Equator. Nothing came of it though; times had changed. It had soon become apparent that it would take longer than the three years allocated to reprocess the last of the fuel; but the fast reactor reprocessing plant encountered difficulties and never re-opened. All that was left of operations was fuel fabrication – and that came to a halt in 1998 when it was decided to call time on the plant after the safety audit of that year. From then on all that would be happening at Dounreay would be the cleaning and restoring of the site. Colin Punler, then a journalist and now communications manager at Dounreay, made two remarks at the time that covered much of Dounreay's difficulties. "At the heart of Dounreay's problems of recent years appears the rationale that it should be run as cheaply as possible," and "Fuel plants that were built in the 1950's and which should have been allowed to retire gracefully were hammered into the ground in the 1990's leading to a spate of leaks and contamination scares."

Appropriately, it was just before the start of April Fools' Day of 1994, at about ten minutes to midnight on the 31st of March, that the prototype fast Reactor was closed down for the last time. Some 200 invited guests watched on a closed TV circuit in the main canteen as the reactor was powered down. A dinner followed at the Weigh Inn Motel in Thurso and each guest was given a souvenir Caithness Glass paperweight. From that moment there was no more fast reactor research within the UKAEA.

Sir John Hill (second left) watching Gordon Blagden (extreme left) commencing the closing down procedure for the last time.

RESEARCH AND DEVELOPMENT

Kath Cartwright.

In as large an operation as Dounreay, which has employed in excess of 20,000 people over the years, not all are going to be completely satisfied with working in the complex and there will be a marked difference in work load and attitudes between individuals: yet so many carry happy memories of their time and their place in Dounreay. Each has contributed a little to the history of the place and more than one has commented on their pride in being part of the whole.

Kath Cartwright came to Dounreay in 1982 as a student and first lodged in the Hostel. Born in Darlington from a family that had been in railways for generations, she was always attracted to engineering and science. She received sponsorship from the UKAEA to gain her degree and, later, it was a natural progression to commence work with the Authority. She thought Caithness magical when she first arrived – and this after travelling up by train in the pitch dark and cold of a January night. Very much against the trend of the other graduates taken on by the Authority, she wanted a job at Dounreay. Another student had absolutely refused to come and yet another agreed that he would fly up for a day at a time but he would not stay overnight. Apparently this was considered a reasonable attitude.

But Kath knew what she was coming to. She loved the scenery and she loved the people – and she loved her job. She was put into Research and Development in support of the PFR fuel reprocessing plant with the remit to look at ways and means of improving the separation of reusable fuel from the contaminated residue. The pilot plant concerned in the operation was three storeys high and was, in effect, a giant diffuser where plutonium and uranium were winnowed out as the aqueous mixture that contained them was agitated by air pulses. There were no moving parts in the diffuser and the droplets of the mixture squeezed through ever-smaller apertures as it rose up the giant column.

When Kath had started at Dounreay the civil service atmosphere pervaded everywhere – how large an office you got, how much carpet, whether you had a glass-fronted bookcase, all were subject to detailed regulations. Procedure dominated everywhere.

In the late 80's and early 90's however, Kath was caught up in the fashion for privatisation that swept the Authority. Without leaving her office and without doing other than she would have done she found herself consecutively part of AEA Technology, then Nukem and, finally, returned back to the UKAEA. Today she is a section manager within the Strategy department. She is charged with taking a helicopter view of all the activities related to the smooth rundown and tidying up of Dounreay. This involves network analysis and logistical studies aimed at ensuring that resources are being optimised and that no one part is doing something that could be more effectively carried out in conjunction with another section.

She envisages benefits in this work for the Authority as they are setting a precedent for nuclear plant closures and the experience gained can thus be applied – profitably – elsewhere. However, as with many, she is not without hope that something permanent can still be made of Dounreay beyond a tourist attraction.

SAFETY AUDIT OF 1998

The safety audit published in 1998 proved to be a seminal event in the Authority's history. The audit was undertaken by the Health and Safety Executive and included representation from the Scottish Environment Protection Agency. The audit was precipitated by an unusual incident when a mechanical digger sliced through a major electrical cable feeding the Fuel Cycle Area on the 7th of May of that year and had left that area without normal electrical supplies for some 16 hours.

The results of the audit have often been described as being critical of Dounreay and its standards of management. In truth it was more critical of the reasons behind the Dounreay situation where two strands of government policy had interwoven; there was the ideologically inspired move towards privatisation and then there was the decision to phase out fast reactor technology. This had led to a major rundown of staff within UKAEA and a consequent loss of skills and knowledge. Consequently there had been a need to employ outside contractors to assist in key management roles and the audit stated that this had brought about an over-dependency on these contractors for technical expertise and know-how. The audit recognised this as the major reason why Dounreay was not in a good position to tackle its principle mission, the decommissioning of the site. The audit also recognised the low morale amongst some sections within Dounreay.

Other criticisms stemmed from this and the audit contained 143 recommendations, the last one being a call for an action plan to be prepared to outline how the issues raised would be tackled and when they would be.

The upshot was that from then onwards Dounreay has concentrated exclusively and professionally upon decommissioning, placing aside all other issues. The final report of the Audit Commission was published in 2001 and, on the whole, it demonstrated a satisfactory state of affairs.

LAURENCE WILLIAMS, HM CHIEF INSPECTOR OF NUCLEAR INSTALLATIONS, SAFETY AUDIT OF DOUNREAY – FINAL REPORT 2001

Laurence Williams, pictured on the right, with DFR's Mike Brown.

I believe the Dounreay Site Restoration Plan sets an ambitious but achievable target. It is a significant step forward from earlier plans which envisaged lengthy periods of 'care and maintenance' for many of the important plants, and an overall timescale which would have been several decades longer.

I have seen very considerable progress at Dounreay over the past three years and this is a credit to everyone concerned, particularly the staff at Dounreay. The consents we have granted over the last few months to allow the restart of a number of plants within the Fuel Cycle Area are an indication of our growing confidence that safety at Dounreay is improving.

However, notwithstanding the genuine hard work which has already been done both at Dounreay and UKAEA's other sites to address the audit recommendations, the ability to deliver the site restoration programme will critically depend upon the Authority's ability to recruit sufficient numbers of suitably qualified and experienced people to operate the site and manage the contractors who will be necessary to design and build the new facilities. The management at Dounreay is optimistic about this for the near future, however UKAEA will need to continue its initiatives to recruit and retain the necessary skilled staff to meet the challenges that lie ahead at Dounreay.

A cross section of Dounreay workers

Donald Sutherland checking drums in the Dounreay Cementation Plant.

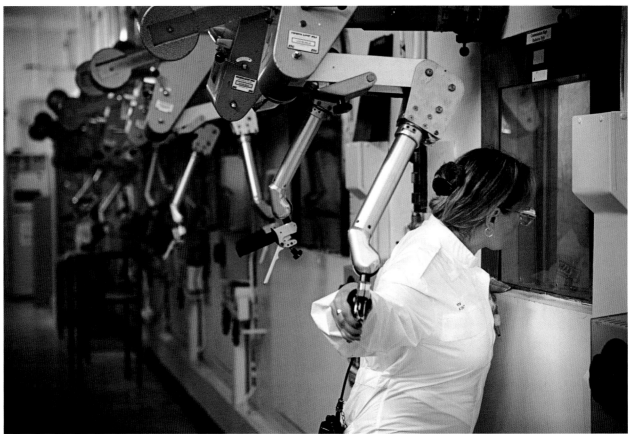

Karen Garbutt using manipulators in the FCA laboratories.

Dougie Mackay in PFR's sodium destruction plant.

Norman Urquhart loads a 'puck' into an ISO container in WRACS.

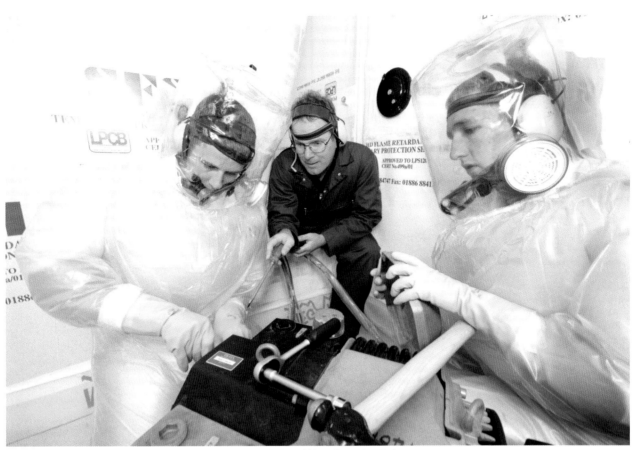

Dounreay apprentices Graeme Mackay and Michael Miller training in airline suits under the watchful eye of trainer Bryan Dods.

Margaret Forbes loading the shelves in the main store.

Eileen Manson, Libby Brown, Zoe Sinclair and Helen Brown sorting letters in the post room.

Debbie Murray and Shirley Mackay serve a hungry customer in the 'Welcome Break' canteen.

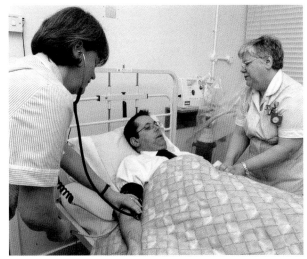

Nurses Marlene Leighton and Isobel Powell practice on a 'live' patient, Alan Coghill.

Members of the Dounreay Fire & Ambulance Service on a training exercise.

A police search officer carrying out vehicle checks at the main gate.

Chapter Twenty-Three
Today

There is nothing more saddening than to walk where once all was noise and bustle and the air was crackling with chat and hope. You can stand above what was once one of the hottest spots on earth, where DFR was situated, right at the heart of the dome. You marvel at and do wonder how the people of yesterday managed to direct such a complex operation without the computer power of today.

The original chimneystack has been replaced by a new one and the original controls – levers and clock faces and push buttons – are all set out as they were when they actually controlled something. The society Historic Scotland did consider making the building a listed one once it has all been cleared out. The future of the dome is uncertain though; the most likely outcome will be that, eventually, it will be demolished and the debris stored as 'low level radioactive waste.'

Perhaps that is as it should be. Why should the dreams and aspirations of generations now gone intrude on generations afresh? And, yet, it is sad.

The visitor centre falls to the demolition man.

Even the visitor centre which was re-established is gone, ripped apart by the demolition team's bulldozers. Some 9,000 people visited it in 2006 (its last year). You could even win a fluffy toy if you manipulated the remote control handler (an exact replica of what was used to pick up radioactive material) properly. Something of the visitor centre and something of Dounreay will remain in the Thurso visitor centre (Caithness Horizons) though. The story of Dounreay is laid out chronologically and the guides are well able to answer questions thrown at them – and, if not, they know where to find the answers.

Dounreay itself is still busy though but it is a different busy-ness. It employs as many as ever. The purpose now is to pull down, clean up, dispose of, store and renew; tasks every bit as demanding as running the operation once was and controlled by thinking, professional people who scan charts, draw up critical path networks, consult lap top computers, set targets, attend crucial meetings and attempt to achieve the aims in the best possible fashion and as cheaply as possible. The skill needed is just the same; the professional commitment given is just the same. The Dounreay Site Restoration Plan of the year 2000 is the most comprehensive, complex and integrated nuclear decommissioning strategy ever produced. The government has pledged to fund the estimated £2.9 billion it is expected to take to finance it through to when the decommissioning is expected to be completed. When the safety audit identified the shortfall in skills at Dounreay hundreds of people were taken on to fill the gap in order that decommissioning could safely commence.

The new objectives at Dounreay are to ensure the long-term safe storage of the radioactive waste, to ensure all the redundant nuclear facilities are decommissioned, that there are no longer any radioactive discharges from the site, that all chemical and radioactive contaminated land is restored, that all unused buildings have been demolished and that all waste – and all is now waste – is managed properly and listed, checked and stored. In short, the UKAEA wants the site returned as near as possible to its pre-Dounreay pristine condition.

In carrying out this role, Dounreay has continued to pioneer techniques and methods relevant to the decommissioning. They have successfully commissioned a new sodium disposal plant and, to date, have established a world record for the amount of sodium destroyed. They have also blazed trails in the development both of water vapour nitrogen technology (for the removal of alkali metal residues) and in the operation of low-level liquid waste assay characterisation. Where once scientists stood on the one side of thick, shielded windows to experiment with plutonium and uranium, now demolition teams in protective suits with breathing apparatus are scrubbing and dismantling from the inside out. Some areas are still too hazardous for people to be in, so robotic equipment is used to commence the work until individuals can safely enter.

Even the famous shaft has to be tackled and emptied.

So Dounreay is still the proverbial hive of activity.

But it ain't the same.

And it ain't the same because there is a definite end in sight. The master flow-chart currently shows the latter half of the year 2032 as the time when all activity beyond monitoring and security and – possibly – tourism will stop at Dounreay.

For over fifty years Dounreay has been a major source of employment, both direct and indirect, in Caithness and it has been assessed as supporting almost 2,500 jobs both directly and indirectly in Caithness and North Sutherland: that is, over 20% of the local employment is Dounreay dependent – a value worth between £70 to £90 million to the local economy. Thus the decommissioning programme has a major impact in Caithness and North Sutherland and places a responsibility on UKAEA to ensure that a significant spend from the decommissioning is used within Caithness to lay down, as far as possible, a foundation for the area's economy once decommissioning is completed.

Caithness, in many ways, is more like an urban area than a rural one in terms of its economy. Whilst agriculture, fishing, small crafts and tourism make up a considerable part of the economy, there is a high concentration of employment in advanced manufacturing, engineering and business services. That is the reason for the long-term concern. By around 2020 it is anticipated that Dounreay will employ only 600 and beyond that the run-down will be rapid.

UKAEA, now officially the clean-up contractor to the Nuclear Decommissioning Authority, is doing its best to mitigate the worst effects. It has been instrumental in setting up a master's degree course in nuclear decommissioning; a qualification now recognised throughout Europe, and has launched various initiatives in conjunction with local bodies aimed at the regeneration of the area.

The test facility at Janetstown, known as t3uk, with the Orkney island of Hoy in the background.

In addition, UKAEA became a tenant of the Forss Science and Technology Park (a few miles east of Dounreay) as part of its drive to create business on the back of its decommissioning expertise and has been involved in constructing a test facility at the local industrial estate at Janetstown in Thurso. Procord, the company who had taken over much of the responsibility for facility management in the 1990's were taken over, in turn, by Johnson Controls, with what was left on site returning or remaining within government dominion.

Johnson Controls is a large, Michigan based American company (turnover in excess of $20 billion) that is involved in a number of industries including the provision of facilities management services that it undertakes at Dounreay. These services include everything from catering through to snow clearance and road gritting. They also handle building maintenance and reception. In fact they list over 90 activities and services they provide for the site.

This extensive privatisation and divestment programme was closely monitored by the various unions who were concerned about the safety aspects of 'outsourcing' and divesting as well as being worried about the kind of employer that was coming in and the terms, quality and future of the jobs on offer.

In fact there is quite a future at Dounreay still. Apprenticeships, perhaps one of the major social and economic benefits that Dounreay brought to Caithness, continue still albeit fewer in number. Gary Davidson, who joined as the 1,000th apprentice taken on by Dounreay since its start (in 2003), is one looking to at least five years with the UKAEA. Though born in Thurso, Gary is a Wicker and has lived there all his a life. His father also works in Dounreay and Gary plays for a local football team. As the new breed of Dounreay employee, he catches the 6.50am bus every morning to the site for his 8.00 o'clock start. Like so many before him he relishes the atmosphere. That was always so with Dounreay. Some people worked hard in it, others less so – some had an easy life if truth be known – but to the vast majority that passed

Gary Davidson, speaking at the apprentices indenture ceremony in November 2004.

through its portals Dounreay represented an important aspect of their life. Even after they left it, individuals still cared and, ever afterwards, considered themselves Dounreay people and of the Dounreay family – family not being too strong a word in this context.

The work to be carried out is as complex and as difficult as any of the pioneering work. It is pioneering work in itself. Cleaning up and restoring is a massive and complex task and bedevilled by the fact that all existing equipment has to be treated as if it is contaminated. Dounreay uses the modern word 'challenge' in their own description of the tasks facing them – they really mean major problems.

But they know how to tackle them.

UNIONS

The changes that enveloped the structure of the UKAEA as it struggled to come to terms with privatisation involved much prolonged discussion with the unions on site. A good and well-run union is a management asset. It eases communication between the shop floor and the boardroom and the boardroom and shop floor. It highlights potential problems before they become serious.

Derrick Milnes.

Derrick Milnes joined the Authority in 1974. He had stayed in Wick during the early war years and he was more than pleased to move back north with his family when he had the opportunity to start in the wages and salaries department. After that he moved into the records department of reprocessing and then into health and safety. He had become interested in union matters early on however and gravitated to being branch chairman of the Civil Service Union. Eventually he was nominated for the National Executive. This was at a critical time for the union movement as the Conservative government was deciding that union membership was inimical to working in secret and semi-secret government establishments. Derrick, although he received the full support of site director Clifford Blumfield, eventually found constant travel to London too much and was content to take over the area chairmanship for the North of Scotland. Later, when John Baxter arrived as site director union activities again flared as the Authority was split into public and private sectors. Derrick believes the team spirit of the old Dounreay was never fully recaptured after private contractors were let in to take over much of the running of the site (he is not alone in that thought). He is also one of those who fought hard to keep something going in Dounreay after the closure of PFR was announced. He still believes that was a mistake (not to have a follow-on to PFR) and that, ultimately, the decision to completely close Dounreay will have to be reversed.

Whilst all this was in the air, he had been promoted within Dounreay as well and had now a busy and diverse job as well as his union work; thus it was almost a relief when he was approached about taking on the role of dealing with political affairs in the communications department.

Chapter Twenty-Four
The Challenges of Tomorrow

On a beautiful summer's day the public car park for Dounreay is only a pleasant quarter-of-a-mile stroll from the reception building (the car parks are huge and well used so it does depend on where you can find a spot). On a winter's day with the sun not yet up and the infamous Caithness wind whipping around you it can be a two-mile struggle. The road directly leading onto the site and reserved for employees and delivery vans is picked out with short, concrete obelisks designed to stop any would be trouble makers forcing themselves onto the site. And, you have to bear in mind, the policeman in the lodge at the gate is armed –.

It was not always thus but as times change and international terror groups become ever more sophisticated, so do protective strategies become ever more elaborate.

You enter reception. You cannot arrive unannounced. You have to be on the list. You book in and receive your visitors pass. Then you wait until the police have checked your baggage; you sign your name again. Although they are really looking for something sinister, like guns or explosives, cameras are not allowed on site unless by permission. In these days of increasing miniaturisation and dual-purpose devices, keeping cameras out can be difficult. However, the principle is there. It is more a concern about the illicit noting of security arrangements rather than there being any secret of science that lies behind this restriction.

Once collected at reception by your site host, you next have to negotiate the first heavy turnstile to enter inside the first fence perimeter. This is not easy in itself especially if you are carrying a heavy briefcase and you have to shove through whilst at the same time holding up your visitors pass for inspection. Anyway, you're finally in. Dependent on your destination, you may have the next perimeter to pass. This involves changing your visitors pass for another, remembering a code number to tap in and pushing into an even heavier full size turnstile. The weight of these mechanical brutes is deliberate and is designed to stop anyone bursting through with mayhem in mind.

The third step is into areas where radioactive materials lie. Only the fact that others do it everyday without a flinch makes you continue. In fact, it is perfectly safe. You are more in danger from someone dropping a spanner on your head than from picking up a radioactive particle. That's why you don a hard hat at this point. You are also festooned with 'dosimeters' designed to alert to any radiation around.

The change room, where you go "over the barrier".

You take off your shoes, sit on a low bench and, without putting your stocking feet on the floor, swivel round on your backside to the next area where, again without putting your stocking feet on the floor, you slip into the regulation Dounreay shoes having already struggled into the regulation Dounreay coverall. You are in - as they say at Dounreay, "over the barrier" – to the very heart of what had been the output end of the Dounreay experiment.

There is a lot going on; slowly and carefully on. Men are working in special suits within tents with airlines attached – sometimes just to the tent and sometimes to the suit directly. Waste bins are carefully labelled with their contents and time and date. Later they will be compacted in the 'Waste Receipt Assay Characterisation and Supercompaction Facility'(WRACS). Only the civil service could have come up with such a name. They mean the bin crusher.

Returning back "over the barrier" is equally exciting. You divest yourself of your outer overall, swivel over the dividing shelf and, thankfully, return to your own shoes. You wash your hands thoroughly. Then you have to pass through a checking booth to ensure you are not now contaminated goods. This involves placing your hands so and your feet thus and then turning round and pressing up against the mechanism. There is a long slow moment as the female voice (the voice of an employee – physiotherapist Miriam Sutherland), which has been instructing you what to do, begins her countdown; five – long pause –four – long pause –. At last she assures you that you are clear and the tension evaporates. That's when you wonder where you left your briefcase –

The most horrendous task is dealing with the shaft. The project to seal it off from the marine environment is well underway, and required the construction of an enormous concrete working platform, not unlike a war time gun emplacement. Boreholes are being sunk around the shaft in the shape of a boot, which are then filled with grout, which will minimise movement of sea water through the shaft. Once it has been sealed off, it can be emptied. Because of the nature of the shaft and the delicacies of the cleaning involved it is not anticipated that this area will be fully restored until 2031 (in comparison the pond that served DMTR should be emptied and decommissioned by 2008). Much the same procedure will be needed in dealing with the waste silo that was in use until the late 1990's.

The prototype fast reactor is the other major task with some 1,500 tons of sodium requiring to be broken down into salt and water. "We have very significant challenges in decommissioning that reactor," said site director Roy Nelson in what could be described as an understatement. The fundamental strategy is to remove the greatest hazards as quickly as possible and progressively restore the environment to the point where as much of it as feasible can return to normal use. This sounds simple but includes such activities as stabilising the sea-cliff and chemically neutering 57 tonnes of NaK.

As a result of Dounreay parts of the land around will have to be restricted to access for hundreds of years – one good thing, however, was that, in 1998, the UKAEA restored the environs of the old Dounreay Castle. Because of its archaeological importance, this work was carried out under the guidance of Historic Scotland.

And the clean up and restoration will be expensive.

All this throws into sharp perspective the wisdom of nuclear power.

Boreholes being drilled.

The shaft raised working platform, seen from the sea.

IN THE ARCHIVES

Ian Pearson and his staff in the newly fitted-out archives department. Back row: Tanya McGovern, Sharon Cameron – middle row: Ian Pearson, Sheena Campbell, Lindsay Archer, Susan Campbell – front row: Julia Rand, Isobel Swanson.

Like a well integrated orchestra each individual and each section within Dounreay has and have an important part to play that showcases and supports the main activity – like the third trumpet is as important to the orchestra as the whole string section is, so each person and department was as important to the tearing of power from an atom as the reactor itself and, nowadays, to the clearing up operation.

Dounreay could not function if it were not for the supporting services that surround the often more glamorous roles that the engineers and scientists play. Ian Pearson and his staff in the archives department, for example, beaver away without too many taking sight or notice of them and yet they play a vital part. It is their remit to ensure the lessons learnt from the Dounreay experience are recorded and maintained for the benefit of future generations.

All documentation relating to every aspect of Dounreay's multi-varied life is preserved in some way or another in the archives department, thus ensuring posterity can learn from past errors and profit from past successes. Every now and again qualified individuals sift through the documents and précis them in order to keep the fifty years worth of assembled paperwork under some sort of control. The documents are then stored in microfiche or on compact disc.

Ian joined Dounreay initially as a specialist glassblower, another aspect of the requirements of the laboratories, and is a distinguished individual in this field, being the chairperson of the British Society of Scientific Glassblowers and having won many awards for his designs and innovations.

WRACS

The drum going through the inspection system.

The bin crusher is a massive plant specially built for the decommissioning process. The drums are handled on a production flow basis. The details of each drum are recorded and the drum enters the conveyor belt based inspection system. It is first x-rayed to check the contents and all x-ray plates are retained as part of the drums ongoing identity check. There is both a scanner for gamma activity and also alpha activity. The penultimate stage of this machine is where the drums, some containing heavy concrete pieces, are squashed using a massive 2,000-tonne force. The drums are prevented from bursting sideways in this part so the only way they can go is downwards. This process guarantees a reduction of the size of the 200-litre drum down to a fifth of its size but, in practice, it can be compressed further depending on what is in it. Finally the compacted drum (now termed a 'puck') is transferred into a container via a grab mechanism. Once the container is full (it too is numbered and identified) it is lidded and driven to a monitoring and inspection area.

Chapter Twenty-Five
The Dark Side of the Force

Nuclear power is well understood and is a relatively safe way of raising energy.

That may need to be said again because it cuts across the pre-conceived perceptions of so many; nuclear power is well understood and is a relatively safe way of raising energy.

What is not safe, by no means safe, in fact is incredibly unsafe are the human beings who operate and control it. They can be lazy, they tire easily, make mistakes, let their passions and emotions overspill their objectivity, become garrulous, intrigue in politics and can be vain, delusional and petty. Finally they can just be downright stupid. Not the ideal creatures to run a nuclear plant or, indeed, anything.

But they are all that we have and, on the other hand, they can rise to great heights as well.

Not that nuclear power is free from inherent danger. That was not grasped in the beginning when Roentgen's discovery of x-rays led to both a misuse and an over-use of them. X-rays promised much and achieved much. They were an astonishing advance in medicine. However, even before the end of the 19th century many of the practitioners who dealt with them had already died of cancer.

The most famous victims of their own research into radioactivity were Pierre and Marie Curie. Pierre died in a bizarre street accident when a bolting dray horse in Paris ran him down in 1906. Then again, he already suffered from cancerous sores and how long and what quality of life he would have had is problematical; although Marie Curie lived to 67, it was to leukaemia she succumbed in 1934. And there were many less illustrious scientists who quietly died of cancer of one sort or another after dealing with a radioactive source. A glassblower became one of the first victims in 1904. He formed x-ray tubes and tested them on his hands. He suffered skin cancer on both hands and even amputating them did not stop the spread of the evil disease.

Cancer has some superficial qualities akin to the slow burning of paper. Leave paper long enough and it goes brown at the edges, wrinkles up and, finally, breaks into shreds (ash). Cancer spreads in a similar fashion in the body – like a slow burn.

It took a while for the danger to be realised. Radium was not licensed and businesses began to use it in a variety of ingenious ways. It was even sold as a health benefit – a general pick-you-up. It was not until the 1920s that the high incidence of cancer amongst radium painters – individuals employed to put radium paint onto anything from dolls' eyes to clock faces – alerted the fact that there was a connection between radiation and cancer. Many of them developed cancer of the mouth and tongue area from a habit of pointing their brushes in their mouths. Incredibly though, radium was still being used for watch faces as late as the 1960s.

The full horror that radiation and nuclear power could produce however was amply displayed in the Japanese cities of Hiroshima and Nagasaki. The ongoing radiation effects of those nuclear bombs had not been expected. The use of the bombs also imbued the public with an awareness and fear of the dark side of nuclear power and gave a suspicion thenceforth to all activities involving nuclear power.

But, even then, scientists could be blasé. Physicist Louis Slotin accidentally assembled a critical mass in his hands whilst demonstrating criticality to students and visiting scientists. Slotin died within two weeks.

Dwight D. Eisenhower could talk, in 1953, of turning swords into ploughshares and that was the epithet attached to a statue of Man at the new United Nations building but it did not hide the fact that ploughshares could also be fashioned into weapons and, in the case of nuclear power, pretty powerful ones at that. Robert Oppenheimer was one who came to oppose the manufacture of such weapons and declared that the attitudes adopted by the United States and the Soviet Union were the same as those of 'two scorpions in a bottle.'

And, because of the political situation of the time, all the new nuclear research and development institutions, whatever else they did, had a section participating in the development of weaponry.

This may or may not have been necessary but it, in turn, spawned an excessive secrecy around nuclear power – a secrecy that, in the long term, harmed such as Dounreay. Civil servants and administrators are by habit secretive but the nature of nuclear power provided them with even more justification for this practice (in their eyes).

Windscale, in the north of England, suffered a severe accident in October 1957. Windscale was used at the time for the production of weapons grade plutonium. Due to shortcomings in the instrumentation the control staff mistakenly boosted the heat in the reactor when, in fact, they needed to reduce it. Temperatures soared to over 380 degrees Celsius. The resultant fire released a massive dose of radioactive material that was carried over the north of England. It has subsequently been estimated that possibly up to 33 persons could have died prematurely as a result of cancer from the incident. At the time though, the Government fibbed about the scale of the accident. Longer-term they would have been better advised to tell the truth.

Following this there was a steady stream of incidents in nuclear plants. The Enrico Fermi Atomic Power Plant had been crippled by technical problems from the start and with a series of sodium fires. It did not start supplying electricity until 1966 – and then, three months later, it self destructed when the reactor had to be scrammed. No one was harmed and the safety back up performed superbly but $120,000,000 had been spent to produce a few thousands of dollars worth of electricity. Although it did restart in 1970, it was shut down finally in 1972. Shortly after the Windscale happening, an explosion took place in the plutonium production plant in the Urals. Little detail is still known of this but it has been alleged that hundreds were killed as a result.

Then there was the Three Mile Island incident – Three Mile Island being a plant near Pennsylvania. Again this accident was the result of faulty equipment. A valve had become lodged open and cooling water continued to pour away for over two hours. This failed to register visually on the main control panel. Once it was recognised that the relief valve was open a valve upstream of the relief one was closed permitting the chance to gain some sort of control. About an hour-and-a-half later the out of core flux meters recorded increases heralding the slumping of several tonnes of molten fuel. It took a further eleven hours before forced coolant circulation could be achieved, essentially halting the incident. The plant came within hours of a full-scale meltdown and it was only a fresh supervisor arriving on the scene who deduced what was happening that saved the situation. Yet, even so no lives were lost and no radioactivity was released.

Unlike Chernobyl in Ukraine in April 1986.

Chernobyl killed some thirty persons immediately and is and will be responsible for, perhaps, the early deaths of many more (the future death toll is a much argued over figure but the Ukraine Radiological Institute suggests up to 2,500 premature deaths as a result of the radiation leaked whereas Greenpeace puts the figure over one hundred thousand). The reasons for the accident are not perfectly known since much of the evidence is irrecoverable. It all began when a test was being undertaken to check if the turbines could produce enough power to keep the coolant pumps running until emergency diesel back-up generators could come in to take over.

Incredibly, in order to run the test undisturbed, many safety systems were switched off. The test ran at night with a minimum staff on. It had been intended to cut the reactor to 25% of its power. Instead (for unknown reasons) it fell to almost one per cent and then surged up again. Unknown to the crew (and counter-intuitive) the reactor was more dangerous at lower power. In technical terms it had a dangerously large positive void co-efficient. This meant that bubbles of steam had probably formed in the reactor coolant and speeded up the nuclear reaction. The emergency shut down procedure simply did not proceed to emergency shut down. Within less than a minute the reactor went out of control. A massive steam explosion lifted the 1,000 tonne sealing cap on the reactor building and other explosions followed.

The weakness may well have been in design. The lowering in of the control rods as part of the shutdown procedure, if too many are dropped in at once between the fuel rods, can, momentarily, increase the power before the dampening effect takes place. The lower end of the control rod, being graphite, displaces water (which is denser and a neutron absorber, as opposed to graphite which is a neutron moderator) and thus can cause a brief increase in power before the desired effect of decreasing the reaction kicks in. Although this was already understood elsewhere, it

has been doubted if the operating crew in Chernobyl were aware of this phenomenon and they possibly threw all the control rods in at once.

There have been other accidents in nuclear power plants around the world since – most notably in Japan. The worst Japanese accident happened at Tokaimura when shortcuts were indulged in. A critical mass of enriched uranium was brought together by workers mixing nitric acid and oxide of uranium in buckets (yes, in common buckets) and pouring the mixture directly into a sedimentation tank. The mixing was supposed to have been carried out in special containers before being poured into the tank in carefully controlled amounts with automated procedures to ensure a critical mass could not be dispensed. The men involved had no awareness of the risks they were taking. What they thought or felt when a flash of blue light filled the room as the air ionised and they realised they had been irradiated cannot be imagined nor described.

Despite all this, nuclear accidents are not frequent (although sometimes not well reported) and produce few direct casualties. Many of the nuclear accidents involve nuclear weapons and nuclear powered submarines and there are suspicions that the United States has had accidents testing nuclear powered flying craft. Although these accidents can be lumped together as nuclear accidents, there is a few degrees of difference in carrying around nuclear material compared to well shielded and permanently sited reactors designed solely to produce electrical power.

Yet, such is the awe that nuclear power is held in, that each accident erodes public support – especially as the finances are not working out in the way the early pioneers of the industry had foretold and nuclear power is proving costly. And then there is all that nuclear waste – most of it low-grade but still an estimated 100,000 tonnes in Britain alone

Does all that mean we should surrender the nuclear dream?

Chapter Twenty-Six
And The Day After Tomorrow

Britain made a decision back in the 1950's. It poured money and research into the nuclear resource. It wasn't the only country to do so. Only Denmark chose to develop a renewable energy alternative in any serious fashion. The result, for Denmark, was good. Today that country is the world leader in wind turbine technology with over sixty per cent of the wind generators sold worldwide being of Danish manufacture.

Perhaps such soft energy options were too mundane for some at the time. Scientists, politicians and, indeed, people everywhere were eager to explore nuclear power. Scientists had by then a good understanding of the mechanisms of the atom and how to produce energy from it – and it was glamorous to be at the cutting edge of unravelling the secrets of the Universe. They were understandably eager to advance their theories and learning and apply it in a practical form.

Were they right to go ahead? It was only by experimenting with such new technologies in such places as Dounreay that shortcomings and advantages, if there were any, could be revealed. In the event it was demonstrated that scientists and engineers knew how to produce the power but failed to grasp the type of systems required to use and control it and how to properly deal with the inadvertent residue it left behind.

What the nuclear experiment taught us was, as with all experiments, more about ourselves than anything else.

Of course there was the military side to nuclear development. The bomb was prestigious. Only the leading countries had the bomb. It marked them as important nations and deterred aggressors – and it did its bit for a forced peace amongst the powerful nations. The civil use of nuclear power gave this horror, necessary or otherwise, a fig leaf of respectability. But it also muddied the waters with regard to the peaceful applications of nuclear energy. Much of the waste and many of the mistakes made were related to the military use of nuclear power, not the civil use; but the difference between the two was hard to distinguish – particularly for the layman.

Part of that military build-up was the development of nuclear submarines. The benefits are obvious. Submarines, armed to the teeth with nuclear missiles, could stay submerged almost indefinitely without any need to refuel. The down side was just that; submarines could only sink. Nuclear reactors are highly dangerous (that might seem obvious but when you work with something on a daily basis, no matter what, you can get blasé) and need massive protection even when they are static; to use them to power any transport is a high-risk business.

Yet, paradoxically, haulage is where much of the future of nuclear power lies. At some stage we will step out into the depths of our solar system. Our curiosity will drive us to see for ourselves what is on the other worlds of our system and what benefits we will gain by going there. And the power that will get us there, operating safely in the depths of space, will be nuclear. It will be nuclear power that will drive our great ships between the planets and their moons; it will be nuclear power that will light and heat the bases we will eventually build on the Moon and on Mars.

It can be no other.

And there will also be a role here on Earth for nuclear fission power – short-term perhaps until better alternatives are developed, but a role it can play now. Thanks to experimental stations like Dounreay much has been learnt. Any nuclear power station built now will reflect those lessons and be constructed to higher standards and, importantly, be bounded by stricter controls and procedures.

That still leaves the perpetual problem of dealing with the radioactive waste such a station exudes. Even that is not as bad as it once was. It has been estimated that a regular nuclear power station set to produce in the 1,500 megawatts range would create waste of around 25 to 30 tonnes per annum.

Methods of storing this waste have improved considerably of late. There is a whole set of new vitrification techniques now available (the Scandinavians are even storing in copper) that extend the time such material can be held safely whilst the radioactivity dissipates. Previously much waste of this kind was stored in concrete – a method with a limited life span (estimated at slightly more than two hundred years) – and thus one that requires that the waste be re-housed relatively frequently until it is deemed safe. There are also fears concerning this method to the effect that, eventually, the concrete will fracture and waste could then contaminate groundwater.

A relatively new process, already trialled in America although invented in Britain and termed geomelting, is claimed to keep such material vitrified for over 200,000 years.

Even if geomelting proves successful and practical it is not a perfect solution to the waste problem but, if so, will prove a more effective solution than existing methods and will remove much of the concerns regarding the use of nuclear fission for peaceful purposes.

Even so, any power raising means that creates such waste can only be used on a limited scale and for a limited time until some other and waste free form is developed.

The other problem is cash. On the basis of direct running costs nuclear power is generally well below the price of fossil fuels. Nuclear power currently generates something like 16% of the world's electricity and does so at about 40% of the cost of oil and gas. Only coal is comparable. But then there are the construction costs of nuclear power stations to be taken into consideration and the cost of storage of waste thereafter. Much of the balance between fuel costs depends on how long the nuclear plant is viable for. Thanks, in part, to the work carried out at Dounreay a modern nuclear reactor could have more than sixty years of life to enjoy and, with the advanced containment processes being applied to the waste, would then have a chance of comparing overall with fossil fuels in cost.

Even so that is still an unfair comparison. It does not take into account the hidden costs of fossil fuels that manifest themselves in the health services of the world and that are the consequences of the burning of such fuel. We have been using fossil fuels so long that we forget there burning exudes all kinds of waste products – including radioactivity – that are innately damaging to life forms. Cancers, respiratory problems, heart diseases and even skin conditions can all be traced back to the effluent from fossil fuel power stations. The cost of these illnesses to the community is intangible and incalculable but is, nevertheless, real. If the burning of fossil fuels had been a recent invention we would never have gone down that route but reacted in horror to the toxic wastes such a process produces and to the high (much higher than the nuclear industry) death tolls involved.

And then, if we worry about the residue from nuclear waste, there is the residue from fossil fuels and the direct link they have to global warming to consider.

The Intergovernmental Panel on Climate Control (The IPCC – a United Nations organisation) have clearly stated that global warming is happening and that it is the result of Man's activities; to whit, the releasing of billions of tonnes of greenhouse gases into the environment. The long-term effect of this is unpredictable. The Irish scientist John Tyndall (1820-1893) first predicted such an occurrence in 1863. He suggested that the nature of the gases being released (essentially methane and carbon dioxide) would bring about a similar end result as a greenhouse does. The sunlight streams down during the day and heats our planet. Normally this heat is radiated away at night; thus keeping the planet's temperature within a range. Greenhouse gases in the atmosphere still permit sunlight to stream down through them (as glass in a greenhouse permits the sun's rays to do) but bounce back the infrared radiation that normally deflects from our planet into space (as the greenhouse glass deflects the internal heat of the greenhouse back inside it). The process is not as smooth as that and the analogy with a greenhouse is not perfect but broadly, that's how it works. In the past there were natural mechanisms that took these gases out of the atmosphere. Those mechanisms are still there but we are overwhelming them with the sheer volume of the effluent we emit. In the 19th century there were around 280 parts per million of carbon dioxide in the atmosphere; today there is over 400.

This sort of thing has happened on our planet before but never at such a rate – at least not for the last 65 million years when some 90% of all animal life perished as a result of the planet wide changes that occurred.

The outcome of this global warming may not be that severe but will be disastrous enough.

And that is down to the burning of fossil fuels.

Put bluntly, fossil fuels are the most dangerous fuels we can use – and they are running out. Current estimates give the lifetime of our coal reserves as less than 300 years, oil less than 100 and gas less than 150. These figures must be taken as rough estimates but they do underline the fact that these natural products are finite. Does that leave the door open for nuclear power?

There are, however, renewable fuel options to consider.

Chapter Twenty-Seven
Alternative Energies

Unfortunately the so-called green fuels are diffuse and difficult to harness effectively. Enough sunlight hits our planet to furnish our energy needs 20,000 times over – if we could only collect it and bring it to a point of use.

We currently use the energy equivalent of over 10,000 million tonnes of oil a year with renewable energy taking up less than ten per cent of that total. Nuclear power produces even less – about 7% of the world's energy. We have two problems facing us; the onset of global warming means we must reduce or eliminate our excrescence of greenhouse gases and, because we are running out of fossil fuels anyway, we must find practical alternatives.

We are, of course, profligate in our usage and likely to continue to be so. The biggest hope for our future rests not so much in us curbing our appetite for energy but in our controlling it. This brings into play more intelligent design of our buildings, better insulation, improved materials and, concerning our transport, more efficient engines and more reliance on communal transport (which will therefore have to be comfortable and cheaper).

Easy to say but not so easy to do.

But even implementing conservation measures will not void the need for other energy sources. Waterpower, by virtue of being the oldest energy source used by man, is the most developed. Water mills were grinding corn in ancient Egypt. Their modern descendents are today's hydroelectric installations that pump out almost 20% of the world's electrical requirements with individual hydroelectric stations capable of producing 10,000 megawatts. The one currently being constructed on the Yangtse River is expected to produce 19,000 megawatts of electricity.

It has been calculated that world production of electricity by this means currently represents only one-fifth of what could be achieved – and, recently, new thoughts concerning hydropower may increase that figure. Small is beautiful and mini-hydro systems are now being investigated; power plants that will supply local villages from the local stream. Again China leads in this respect with almost 100,000 such plants already installed.

Water energy also reaches us by the currents and by waves. Caithness's battered shores testify to the power of waves. Waves are erratic, however, and the sea a harsh environment. Devices applied to extract energy have to sustain a considerable pounding. The World Energy Council estimates that up to one-sixth of the world's energy demand could be harvested from waves – but major finance has never been invested and it is only now that the potential is being investigated.

Ocean thermal energy is unlikely to be as controversial. This involves raising energy by exploiting the differences in temperature between the surface waters and water at depth. A device rather like the inverse of a heat pump can convert temperature difference into power to produce electricity. Although this idea appears to hold great promise, the concept is still at an early stage.

Which is all the opposite of solar power where a lot of research and development has been applied.

'Headland' by Frank Begg *(reproduced by kind permission of the artist)*.

A Forss wind turbine before being erected *(reproduced by kind permission of John Keeton).*

Sunlight can be converted into energy even by small-scale devices such as our desktop calculators. Archimedes grasped the power of the sun in the second century in his inspired defence of Syracuse when the Romans came to call. He used shiny contraptions (they may have been enlarged shields) to concentrate light on the sails of the Roman ships. The Romans grasped the power of the sun also when their sails burst into flames.

Similar tools are used today (slightly more sophisticated) where the sun's rays are brought to a point through which fluids are passed to carry away the heat and generate steam to drive turbines. An advance on this has already been outlined. It is an ambitious scheme to position a satellite in geo-stationary orbit that can trap energy from the sun and beam it back to earth.

Back to earth; perhaps one of our best long-term hopes for abundant and clean energy lies in the earth itself. Only a mere three thousand or so miles beneath our feet a great pool of molten rock (magma) is slopping around at temperatures of up to 7,000° Celsius. Sometimes we catch the pinkie tip of this raw power when we see a volcano erupting.

The exploitation of this power is centuries old. The Romans used it to heat bathhouses and, today, the Icelanders are drilling six miles down to tap into this wealth. In the United States this method provides more power than all their wind farms and sun-trapping systems put together. The world's largest power station of this kind is the 'Geezers' in California. Geothermal energy has this advantage over wind and wave; it can be obtained from a point source.

Wind power shares with solar power the honour of being the most researched and developed of the alternative energy strategies. Current improvements in the technology of producing electricity from wind have brought it very near in cost of oil and gas. Wind power produces around 20,000 megawatts worldwide and that figure is increasing daily. Again it is an old technology. Sail mills were used in ancient Babylon. In England, in the 19th century, over 10,000 windmills dotted the land. However, there is a limit to what can be produced from wind.

Finally, in this litany of renewable energy alternatives, there are biomass generators. These can take many forms but basically consist of generators that are fuelled by fast growing crops (such as willow coppice) that take in as much carbon dioxide when they grow as they exude when used as a fuel.

Despite the number of these options available, renewable energy is not yet ready to take over the supply of 70% of our energy needs – to leap from providing less than ten per cent to 70% and oust greenhouse gas producing fossil fuels. Only one fuel supply is currently placed to do that – with all its faults – and that is nuclear. We may have to accept a limited use of nuclear fission power until such times as we have developed renewable green energy options and they become fully viable.

But will the development of green energy sources spell the end of nuclear power and of Dounreay and, indeed, of the high times of Caithness? Ah, there is another option.

The awesome power of the sea battering the Caithness coast.

Chapter Twenty-Eight
The Pentland Firth

Caithness has a massive resource off its shore that it shares with the Orkney Islands. This is the Pentland Firth, one of the most notorious and respected waters in the world. It is not a firth in the true definition; it is a strait that separates the Orkney Islands and Caithness. For all its fame, it is not large a mere 17 miles of sometimes wild water that runs from Dunnet Head in Caithness as its westerly point, to the small scatter of islands at the easterly point named the Pentland Skerries. The distance between Caithness and the Orkneys varies from around six to eight miles and the islands of Stroma and Swona sit in the channel.

The Pentland Firth is the channel where the Atlantic surges in to meet with the North Sea. In the old days sailing boats would chose to take the longer route around the north of Orkney rather than face the Pentland Firth. Even today formidable modern vessels can be pushed off course and run into trouble in the Firth.

And that is because of the power in the tides of the Pentland Firth.

The tides in the Pentland Firth can run up to an incredible 12 knots and even 16 knots has been recorded in certain corners of the Firth. This equates to a massive amount of energy – possibly sufficient, could it ever be harnessed, to power the whole of Europe. And this is one of the reasons why the Pentland Firth is special. The Robert Gordon University in Aberdeen has calculated that 15 terawatt hours per annum is the ultimate than can practicably be obtained from the Firth. A terawatt hour is equal to one billion kilowatt hours and this load represents around 40% of Scotland's annual requirement. The University considers something like 6,000 direct jobs would be created.

The other exciting aspect of the Firth is that the tide almost never stops. There are only brief moments when it turns that its power drops to a very little. Thus the flow of water is predictable as the tide causes them, unlike wave energy or wind power. The known history of such tidal power stretches back into the early Middle Ages but it is certain that such power was used long before that. Tidal mills used a head pond that would be filled by the incoming water and then slowly released to turn a wheel to grind grains. There was a famous such mill situated on London Bridge in the 17th century that took a good deal of its power from the tidal movements of the Thames.

In more recent times the first commercial tidal plant was constructed at La Rance, near St. Malo, in France in 1965. This is a tidal barrage system that uses twenty-four 10-megawatt bulb type turbine generators and it is still operating. The French engineers reckon that if all the tides in the world were to be so harnessed, the world would slow its rotation by 24 hours every 2,000 years.

Of late other prototype tidal power plants have been tested. In 2003 a small station was established in Devon (a 'meagre' 300 kilowatt) and a Norwegian one in Hammerfest followed also at 300 kilowatt.

Hammerfest is a little different to the other two schemes in that it uses tidal turbines rather than a barrage to generate electricity. These marine turbines work much as wind generators do on land except they are submerged. This is the type of scheme most appropriate for the Pentland Firth.

Harnessing such power will not be easy and, as with everything involving work at sea, the cost will be in proportion. Some early surveys have already been undertaken and a difficult road lies ahead as to decide how the potential resource can be exploited and where the best sites are around Orkney and the coast of Caithness for capturing the power; equally there is the problem of transporting such power south. The energy may have to be stored in the form of hydrogen fuel cells. The time-scale will be in years.

Yet much of the underpinning infrastructure is there. Caithness has many substantial and highly capable engineering companies within its boundaries that grew up and learned with Dounreay. Already they are looking beyond Dounreay and the expertise they have gathered with particular reference to decommissioning nuclear reactors. They can sell that know-how worldwide, and they do, but the Pentland Firth is on the doorstep and any project there would be a delight to them.

And the fact that we can consider the Pentland Firth as an opportunity for Caithness is partly due to the success of Dounreay.

And the expertise garnered via Dounreay may even stretch into yet more exotic areas.

Chapter Twenty-Nine
A New Hope

Six large wind generators look down on Dounreay from the east. As they lazily turn over they seem to say, 'We are the present and the future. We are clean. You were not.'

Dounreay's remoteness, the factor that helped it gain its nuclear experimental station, is now the major factor against its continuation. The placing of a nuclear power station there has a number of disadvantages, not least the amount of travel involved.

Travel for both people and the electricity it generates. Transmission losses on power lines are still high despite improvements (figures vary widely and wildly according to load and distance but, conservatively, around 8% in the UK grid system) and the electricity has over one hundred miles to travel south before joining the rest of the grid.

Yet, if we do not develop Dounreay into other areas and continue with its shutdown programme as the final act – what a waste of resources. Much infrastructure is still present at Dounreay, including a highly skilled staff and workforce and Dounreay is still a licensed nuclear site and, crucially, still supported by the local community. With fossil fuel both

discredited and dangerous and the soft energy options not yet ready to take over large-scale supply, nuclear power remains the only other option – although power generation by nuclear fission now seems impracticable at Dounreay as suggested, the Pentland Firth beckons. Whatever route we take however, the generation of energy in a usable and clean form will cost money – lots of it – and the most expensive option is to continue with fossil fuels.

We still need to experiment therefore. We still have to find the Holy Grail of science – abundant supplies of clean and cheap energy.

There is nuclear fusion.

Nuclear fusion is the name given by scientists to the process whereby nuclei (the cores of atoms) melt together with an incoming particle to form a more massive nucleus – rather than splitting to pieces as with fission. Nuclear fission generally (and in nature) takes place in the larger atoms – atoms with high atomic numbers and with cores densely packed with protons and neutrons. Nuclear melting together involves small nuclei as they fuse with a particle to form a larger nucleus. As with

JP05j-228

The JET torus, Europe's fusion experiment at Culham.

nuclear fission, nuclear fusion also involves a loss of mass and, hence, brings about a release of energy. In fact, the fusion of hydrogen brings about a loss of mass of 0.62% (hydrogen –2 fusing to helium-4). This is not much but is still 11 times more than the fission of uranium.

This gives nuclear fusion several advantages over fission. Apart from being more effective, it can be produced from the commonest element in the universe, hydrogen. It is considerably safer with no atmospheric disadvantages in the way of polluting gases and waste materials nor will there be any need to transport hazardous materials on or off site. The radioactivity caused by the speeding neutrons produced is short-lived and provision for long-term guarding and storage is thus not needed.

It is this energy, nuclear fusion, which drives the stars.

That is the problem with it though. So far as we know, the only fusion that occurs naturally in the Universe happens in the stars and, until now, you needed the mass of a star to create such a force of gravity to create the heat (over 15 million degrees Celsius in the centre of our sun) that forces the nuclei together to bring about fusion. When fusion happens in the sun, as it does continuously, we benefit by the energy that streams out and warms our planet and brings life to it.

That massive temperature is needed to breakdown the repulsion each positively charged nucleus has for every other nucleus and to climb through the electron barrier. The need for such energy to prime the fusion process has been a massive obstacle to the development of fusion power.

It is being tried in a site in France though.

At Cadarache, near Aix-en-Provence, the International Tokamac Experimental Reactor (ITER – not by coincidence meaning 'the way' in Latin) is planned. When built it will be a ten storey high building housing the first attempt at a fusion reactor capable of producing electricity on a meaningful scale. The participants are the European Union, the United States, the People's Republic of China, Japan, South Korea, the Russian Federation and, last but certainly not least, Switzerland. The cost has been estimated at $15 billion and it is hoped to be in action by 2015 generating a maximum 500-megawatt. Many of the concepts and materials to be used were first tested at Dounreay.

What is intended is to achieve truly awesome temperatures (up to 100 million degrees Celsius) in order to fuse together the nuclei of the atoms of hydrogen they extract from the water of the surrounding sea. The fusion reactions will take place in a torus – a doughnut shaped vacuum vessel – round which the hydrogen plasma will circulate under magnetic confinement. If all goes to plan the plant will be the first fusion one to achieve criticality: and the good thing is that only one kilo of the hydrogen plasma fuel will provide as much energy as about 70,000 barrels of oil.

The plant is not intended to be a commercial one but one of the matters being investigated will be the economics of building it, running it and tidying up afterwards – although this tidying operation will not be nearly as expensive as Dounreay's because of the low radioactivity involved.

There are other methods of fusion being considered. 'Cold fusion' has been talked of for years and this concerns efforts to achieve fusion at normal temperatures. Some claims have been made with regard to progress – particularly in respect of 'bubble fusion' – but the issue is still much debated. Bubble fusion is the name given to a fusion reaction that may or may not occur during sonoluminescence – an extreme form of acoustic cavitations. This process produces extremely high temperatures – simulations suggest that the centres of the collapsing bubbles may equal those at the centre of the Sun for very brief moments in time. Various groups are now looking at this phenomenon to consider the claims made by the early researchers. It is far too soon to be even hopeful about it but, if bubble fusion proved practical, then it would be a significant step in the production of clean, cheap and portable nuclear energy.

All these possibilities again strengthen the case for research into nuclear energy still to be pursued.

And beyond fusion there are even more exotic possibilities. Hydrino power has its supporters. This is still highly controversial and involves the electron in a hydrogen atom revolving even more tightly around the atoms core and releasing a burst of energy as it drops to the lower state. This is in apparent contradiction to quantum theory and may prove an illusory source of energy.

The greatest energy release our science knows of however – and can contemplate no greater – is the energy released when matter and antimatter collide.

Antimatter is composed of atoms made up of elementary particles that are exactly the same as the ordinary electrons, protons and neutrons that constitute every day matter except that they have an opposite charge. Whereas an electron is considered to have a negative charge, its antimatter equivalent is a positron with a positive charge and the antimatter equivalent of the neutron and the proton are called, unimaginatively but clearly, the antineutron and the antiproton. The antineutron, although electrically neutral, has a magnetic moment opposite to that of the neutron.

When an antimatter particle meets with its opposite matter particle, the event signals the end for both of them with their respective masses turning completely into energy in line with Einstein's famous equation. When physicists at CERN (the European Laboratory for Particle Physics) first created an antiatom of antihydrogen it lasted a nail biting forty-billionths of a second before it came into contact with ordinary matter and was annihilated.

When this type of reaction takes place an awful lot of energy is released. There is a problem though. There is always a problem. Since, as far as we know, the entire universe is a matter universe, there is no source of antimatter beyond what we manufacture; and to manufacture antimatter needs far more energy than we would gain from it.

Ah! There is always a catch. But that is just now; someday perhaps – and there is something else; another source of energy even more esoteric.

The gods have laughed at Man's feeble attempts to master the nature of the atom and extract energy from it.
At times they have cachinnated on the edges of their seats and tears of pure merriment have coursed their cheeks at the follies and stumblings of humans as those creatures have burnt their collective fingers on concerns nuclear.
But behind that laughter, deep and masked, there is a nervousness, an anxiety because Man has learned and is learning; hesitatingly and only a little, but he is learning. One hundred thousand years ago he knew nothing of the atom. Today he knows some of its secrets; today he has glimpsed something of the complex structure of the Universe and the matter and energy that comprises it and the strangeness of quarks and branes and dark matter that may inhabit it.
And of the void in which all may float and where only time and space play; where there may be no rules and time may carry any which way and energy, a weird quantum energy may exist possibly as a result.
It is transient, it is a glimpse, it is uncertain but that is why there is disquiet in the laughter of the gods.
Man is learning, thanks to institutions like Dounreay with all their faults, and if he ever gains even a little control over that quantum energy then he would not have to sneak it from the table of the gods because he would be sitting there – and the table would be his.

Author's Afterword

It has been both a delight and a privilege to write this book; a delight because in so doing I have met with so many Dounreay employees and ex-employees and have been impressed by the high calibre of them and the dedication and commitment of each to Dounreay: a privilege because even though in at the edge, so to speak, I have become associated with Dounreay.

Yes, there were many mistakes made and many things went wrong at Dounreay but that must not obfuscate the overall aim, which was to improve humanity's lot by seeking ways to provide cheap, clean and plentiful energy.

And it must not be forgotten that, despite the errors and digressions and despite its shortfalls it did achieve much towards that – what more could be expected.

I am particularly grateful to the following (all employees or ex-employees) who gave freely of their time and whose enthusiasm (more than one stated how proud they were to be connected with Dounreay) helped drive the project along.

In alphabetical order:-
Ed Adam
Elspeth Anderson
Kath Cartwright
Malcolm Clark
Gary Davidson
Danny Doohan
Les King
Jonathon Kirk
Gina MacKenzie
Derrick Milnes
Jill Nicholson
Ian Pearson
Kenny Porteous
Colin Punler
Linda Smith

I owe each and every one of the above an abiding debt of gratitude for their help and encouragement and for the manner in which each freely imparted their knowledge and memories.

I am also grateful to the work carried out by an earlier generation of researchers into the relationship between the town of Thurso and Dounreay. I have borrowed liberally from their work if not downright plagiarized it. They are:-

Derek Bonnar
Kenneth MacKenzie
Diana McNulty
Pauline Revie

I am also deeply grateful to Liz Swanson and Peter MacKenzie of Stephen's Plastics for their time and unstinting help in explaining to me the intricacies of their business.

Also, I am well aware that this book would never have been written if it were not for two indefatigable individuals. It was Clive Richards of the North of Scotland Newspaper Group, whose sheer energy and enthusiasm and ability to facilitate matters are surely without peer, that drove the book, and the unflappable and diplomatic Alistair Fraser (rightly known, albeit unofficially, as the Historian of Dounreay) of the Dounreay Communications Department that nursed it through its many teething troubles. It was also Alistair who, along with Sue Thompson of Dounreay Communications, dredged through the many thousands of photographs available to make an appropriate selection to enhance this book with, and who also added their comments describing and expanding each picture. That was quite a labour and I am deeply appreciative.

Also I would like to record my especial gratitude to James B. Gunn and Terry Page who not only explained the intricacies of reprocessing fuel to me but who, along with others, helped review this work. I am deeply grateful to them and to all who helped.

Although I would love to blame others for any mistakes of fact or interpretation in the text, unfortunately my own shoulders have to bear that burden as I alone am responsible.

Finally, I do hope my reader enjoyed the light romp through the fifty years of Dounreay.

As the motto of PFR says; – **Out of Caithness to the World**

Bibliography

Books on Dounreay

Dounreay: The Illustrated Story – published by the North of Scotland Newspaper Group, ISBN 1-871-704-219
(Text by Stephen Cashmore)

Dounreay: An Experimental Reactor Establishment by Iain Sutherland and published by the author, ISBN 01-328-8787-81

Books on other Nuclear Stations

Framatome: An Industrial and Business Success Story – published by Albin Mitchell Communication, ISBN 2-226-06-212-2-12-708

Proving the Principle: A History of the Idaho National Engineering and Environmental Laboratory, 1949 to 1999 – published by the National Laboratory, ISBN 0-16-059185-6

Harwell: The Enigma Revealed by Nick Hance MBE, published by Enhance Publishing, ISBN 0-09553055-0-0

Books on Caithness

The New Caithness Book by D. Omand published by the North of Scotland Newspaper Group, ISBN 1-871-704-00-6

Wick of the North by F. Fodden published by the North of Scotland Newspaper Group, ISBN 1-871-704-19-7

Voices in the Wind by Ally Budge published by the North of Scotland Newspaper Group, ISBN 1-871-704-19-7

Caithness and the War; 1939-1945 by N.M. Glass published by the North of Scotland Newspaper Group, ISBN 1-871-704-10-3

Books on Science

Einstein: A Life in Science by Michael White and John Gribbin published by Simon and Schuster, ISBN 0-671-71270-5

The Quantum World by J.C. Polkinghorne published by Longmans, ISBN 0-14-013492-1

Other Worlds by Paul Davies published by J. M. Dent & Sons, ISBN 0-460-04400-1

Asimov's New Guide to Science by Isaac Asimov published by Penguin, ISBN 014-0172-130

The Man Who Changed Everything: the Life of James Clerk Maxwell by Basil Mahon published by John Wiley and Sons, ISBN 0-470-86171-1

Other

Motherwell Bridge: the First Hundred Years, 1898 to 1998 by Terry Houston published by Motherwell Bridge holdings, ISBN 0-9531640-0-4

Appendices
Appendix 1

Glossary of Technical Terms.

Technical terms have been kept to a minimum in this book but for those interested some brief explanations are given here.

They are not intended as full-blown scientific descriptions but are designed to provide an overview of the subject.

Atomic v. Nuclear
In the early days, when Dounreay was being constructed, the fashionable word was 'atomic' and folk referred to 'atomic power.'

Since power such as that provided by coal, oil and gas also depend on atomic action – in this instance the action of the electrons surrounding the atom and not the heart of the atom itself – then 'atomic' is a misleading term to apply solely to the power emanating from the heart or core of the atom. Therefore such power has subsequently come to be referred to as 'nuclear power' to distinguish it from that derived from the action of the electrons.

Thus, today, all such power in scientific writings is termed 'nuclear power.'

Energy
Energy is one of the fundamentals of the universe, indeed, of the cosmos. Thus it is impossible to define of itself. Generally physicists describe it in terms of the ability of objects or systems to do work – i.e. energy in the process of transferring from one body to another. Energy takes many forms including chemical energy, thermal energy (heat), electrical energy and nuclear energy. One form of energy can be converted to another, but in any change of energy from one system to another, the total energy involved remains constant. This is termed the conservation of energy.

Nuclear Energy
Nuclear energy stems from either nuclear fission or nuclear fusion – that is, energy from the very heart of the atom, the tightly packed core.

Nuclear Fission
Fission is a term given to the process whereby the heart of the atom, the nucleus, is split into two approximately equal parts with the consequent emission of neutrons, heat and radiation. Fission can occur spontaneously or, as happens in a nuclear reactor, can be brought about by deliberately absorbing a sub-atomic particle into the nucleus – generally a neutron is the chosen particle for this purpose.

Nuclear Fusion
If fission is nucleus splitting, fusion (confusingly similar a term to fission) is nucleus melding where two or more light atomic nuclei meld or merge to form a heavier atomic nucleus with subsequent release of energy. The loss of mass resulting from the fusion of light elements is generally greater than the fission of heavier elements and thus fusion generates far more energy than fission. It is this fusion process that powers the stars and makes them shine.

Nuclear Power
This is the term given to the energy, usually in the form of electricity, generated using a nuclear reactor.

Atomic Pile
Fermi chose the word 'pile' to describe the world's first nuclear reactor. Rods of uranium fuel were interspersed in a 'pile' of graphite blocks. Fermi later regretted his use of the word and said it was due to his lack of command of English. He really meant to disparage what they had built by calling it a 'heap.'

Chain Reaction and Criticality
Any situation where each reacting part adds energy to the system by the reaction and in so doing begets other reactions the same as itself can be called a chain reaction. Chain reactions occur in chemical processes as well as nuclear.

In nuclear terms a chain reaction is a self-sustaining nuclear reaction, for example nuclear fission, in which the products of the reaction initiate the same nuclear reaction in other atoms.

Within a nuclear reactor a chain reaction continues in a controlled fashion delivering known amounts of energy; in a nuclear weapon the chain reaction is deliberately allowed to continue unchecked causing a rapid and massive explosion.

As a chain reaction proceeds its progression is based on the probability that a neutron released in fission will then cause a subsequent fission: should the situation be one where less than one neutron released causes another fission then the rate of fission will decrease and, through time, the fission process will come to an end: this is sometimes referred to as 'sub-critical.' When, on average, one neutron released causes another fission releasing another neutron and so on, then the rate is steady – when this position is achieved that is sometimes termed the point of criticality and when a reactor continues running in such a steady state it is considered to be critical.

Nuclear Reactor
A nuclear reactor is a unit designed to contain all the equipment and material required to produce and sustain nuclear fission or fusion in a controlled fashion with the general objective of extracting usable energy from the process.

Types of Nuclear Reactor
There are two broad types of reactor, the thermal (slow) reactor and the fast reactor. These, in turn, can be subdivided into a number of different categories dependent on their different characteristics.

The thermal reactor has moderating materials that slow the neutrons until they approach the average speed of the surrounding particles. By slowing the neutron down it is more easily absorbed by fissile uranium or plutonium, hence causing the atomic fission. Variations of these power-producing reactors include those that use graphite, heavy water or normal water as moderator.

Fast reactors use fast moving neutrons to sustain the chain reaction and have no moderating material. They require enriched fuel or plutonium to operate as fewer of the neutrons are absorbed by the fissile uranium or plutonium than in a thermal reactor. Some are capable of producing more fuel than they consume, generally producing plutonium as a by-product.

Chemical Reactions
Chemical reactions are explained by today's working model of the atom (and it is only a model, not an accurate portrayal of reality). Chemical reactions are distinct from nuclear reactions in that they only involve the electrons of an atom. Each shell of an atom has a limited capacity to hold orbiting electrons. Thus hydrogen has one electron orbiting its nucleus in its inner and sole shell and helium has two in its inner and sole shell. The

inner shell of any atom is only capable of holding two electrons. Lithium has two in its inner shell but, with its first shell filled, has to have its third electron in its second shell. All the elements have different numbers of electrons all spaced in their appropriate shells. If an atom has its shells, no matter how many, all fully filled with electrons it can be considered as an inert atom as it will, normally, not take part in chemical reactions. If, however, it still has space for one or more electrons (all this structure of electrons explains the structure of Mendeleev's Periodic table) in its outer shell (all the inner shells being filled with it always the outer one that is short if any) then it will readily take part in chemical reactions as it seeks to satisfy the imperative to fill all its shells by sharing electrons with another atom or even other atoms.

Heavy Water

Heavy water comes about due to the existence of an isotope of hydrogen sometimes termed 'deuterium.'

Hydrogen is the lightest and 'simplest' of all elements consisting of one proton and one electron. Deuterium consists of one proton and one neutron as well as the orbiting electron. Consequently deuterium is heavier than simple hydrogen and thus water made up of deuterium is termed 'heavy water.' In scientific circles it is properly called deuterium oxide but heavy water is a term that has come to stay. Ordinary water is considered to have about one deuterium atom to every 6,760 ordinary hydrogen atoms present in it. Heavy water is used in nuclear plants because it can slow down fast neutrons, thereby controlling the chain reaction.

Isotopes

Isotopes can be considered as flavours or varieties of an element. All isotopes of an element share the same position in the atomic table and all exhibit nearly identical chemical properties but have differing physical characteristics.

Each element exists in at least two varieties – every variety having the same atomic number but differing in relative atomic mass (atomic weight). Atomic number is given by the number of protons in the nucleus and it is this number of protons in the nucleus that determines what element the atom is. The mass number is the number of protons and neutrons in the nucleus. Isotopes of the same element differ only in the number of neutrons in their nuclei. Thus hydrogen, the simplest of the elements, has one electron orbiting a nucleus of one proton (and is thus electrically neutral). Hydrogen-2 (deuterium) is one electron orbiting a nucleus of one proton and one neutron. In nature there is one deuterium atom to every 6,760 hydrogen atoms. Hydrogen-3 (tritium) is a greater rarity still and has two neutrons in its nucleus.

Neutron Induced Swelling

This phenomenon is the increase of volume and the decrease of density of materials subjected to intense neutron radiation. Neutrons bombarding the material's structure rearrange its atoms causing build-ups of voids, Wigner energy and general dislocations of atoms from the initial lattice pattern they were set in. This reduces the strength of the material under bombardment and induces brittleness in it.

Wigner Energy

The Wigner Effect is named after its discoverer the Hungarian Eugene Wigner. This is a term used to describe the displacement of atoms in a solid caused by neutron radiation. The neutrons coming in have enough energy to displace atoms arranged in a crystalline lattice   sometimes in a cascade form. The atoms so displaced may not settle back along symmetrical lines in the lattice. These atoms are termed interstitial atoms and they have an energy associated with them rather because, being out of place, they are under tension. If too many are out of place they can release all this potential energy suddenly thus shooting up temperature. This Wigner energy poses a threat unless dealt with by relieving it through gentle heating.

Appendices
Appendix 2

Extract from statement made to Parliament by Duncan Sandys, Minister of Supply, on January 26th, 1953, announcing British fast reactor research.

"The production of electric power from atomic energy raises a number of novel problems. These have been studied in the light of the experiences gained with our graphite piles at Harwell and at Windscale. We have also had the benefit of valuable discussions with the Canadian experts about the results obtained in the operation of their heavy water reactor at Chalk River, Ontario.

"The most certain method of generating power from atomic energy would be to build an improved type of natural uranium reactor enclosed in a pressure shell, the heating produced being transferred by a gas under pressure through a heat exchanger to a conventional electric power generator. As a by-product, this would yield plutonium, which could be used as fuel for further reactors. The potentialities of such a reactor are being studied. If the prospects are shown to be favourable, we shall consider constructing an experimental atomic power station of this kind.

"At the same time, we hope to develop reactors of a more advanced type, known as 'breeder reactors', by reason of the fact that they are designed to produce more fissile material than they consume. To facilitate the study of these methods, a small experimental reactor of this kind is being built at Harwell. It should be completed in a few months' time. Meanwhile, work is proceeding at Harwell and Risley on the design and development of a full-scale breeder reactor, capable of producing substantial amounts of electricity, and we are at present looking for a suitable site for the construction of this plant."

Appendices
Appendix 3

On February 26th, 1954, a few days before the public announcement in Parliament, the Secretary of State for Scotland, James Stuart, met representatives of Caithness County Council and Thurso Town Council to inform them confidentially of developments. This is his brief for that meeting prepared by civil servants at the Scottish Office:

"Remind the representatives that the meeting is held in confidence and that nothing must be said outside until the public announcement is made.

As the representatives know, the next stage in the development of the atomic energy project is the building of a fast breeder reactor. This was announced by the Minister for Supply as far back as January 26, 1953, but necessity for review of the design of this most ambitious project and search for a site has held up a final decision till now. During this period previous informal contacts with the local authorities have taken place and there has also been some discussion in Parliament and in the Press. Most of the difficulties have now been cleared up and an announcement will be made in a few days time that the plant is to be erected at Dounreay.

Choice of site
After a most careful study of the whole of the coastline of Great Britain and Northern Ireland, the Dounreay site has been selected as the most suitable. This is because:

a)   The site is sufficiently remote from centres of population as to provide an adequate safety margin. Reference is made later (para. 4) to the question of safety.

b)   It is located on the sea coast at a point where:
i) relative levels make possible the construction of a sea water pumphouse
ii) the effluent which would arise from the Chemical Separation Plant would enable it to be disposed of in the sea under the same arrangements for similar effluents as have operated successfully for three years at Windscale in Cumberland.

c)   It is on flat ground with an area of 400 acres and with good foundation conditions.

d)   Twelve million gallons a day of good quality fresh water can ultimately be made available.

e)   Transport facilities (roads and Wick aerodrome) and amenities (i.e. shops, schools, etc, at Thurso) are unusually good in relation to a site which itself is so remote.

Safety
It is suggested that this subject be introduced by reading an extract from the proposed public announcement: "The plant will be housed in a large spherical shell; even so, there is a very remote possibility of a slight leakage of radioactivity in the event of a breakdown of certain parts of the plant. The local authorities have been consulted and arrangements will be made with their co-operation as to what should be done in this most unlikely event."

The Secretary of State should then continue that the Dounreay reactor will be of a very advanced design and it will give rise to "scientific and engineering problems which lie far beyond the bounds of normal industrial practices. In any such pioneering work there must inevitably be an element of risk; however careful the designers may be, however far they go to eliminate all of the risks which they can visualise, there must remain a very remote possibility that some risk which they have not been able to visualise may arise and cause an accident. If this happened with a reactor of the type which is built, there is a possibility that radioactive materials might be dispersed from the reactor and drift down-wind away from it in a narrow band so that people living in this limited zone might be exposed to a certain amount of radioactivity. It

is to guard against this very remote possibility that the reactor will be contained in a large steel shell which should prevent the escape of these radioactive materials in the unlikely event of such an accident. There is, however, the even more remote possibility that the accident might cause some light damage to the spherical container and so permit a slight leakage of radioactive materials from it. If this happened, there would be no danger to life, but it might be necessary to evacuate people living in a narrow sector of land down-wind from the reactor."

(At this point it is suggested that copies of the map attached to A.E. (M)(54)2 should be circulated. The copies of the map should be withdrawn afterwards on the pretext that the population figures are not up to date.) It should be heavily stressed that an accident could only affect one of the segments of land shown on the map. Permanent evacuation would, at worst, be limited to the inner circle shown on the map (much the greater part of which will be occupied by the project itself). The outer circle refers only to a temporary evacuation. On this question of evacuation, there will be the closest consultation between the future AEA and the local authority. It will be necessary however to have control of milk production for a few days up to a distance of about 20 miles from the site.

The Secretary of State may wish to emphasise:

a)   that these dangers will not exist until the plant is working i.e. for another four years. (While we are being very frank with the local authorities it is most desirable that nothing should be said outside which would alarm public opinion four years before anything can happen. If any questions about Thurso are raised, Mr Kendall should be asked to reply.)

b)   During the four years before the plant comes into operation, design will have progressed much further and it is very possible that additional features may be incorporated which will go far to eliminate any such risks as there are at present.

c)   Even however if the plant were going into operation tomorrow on the basis of the existing design, the risks outlined are remote. No atomic energy plants are quite free from risk though plants have worked in this country and in North America for many years without damage to the surrounding populations. Many of these plants were, as this one is, revolutionary and unknown when they were first designed.

Employment
The local authorities will probably be most interested in the question of employment.

a)   Contribution to employment
The Secretary of State may like to stress the value of the project to the area. Unemployment has been a long standing problem in the Wick-Thurso area and ranges seasonally from 430-650, mostly men. While the atomic energy project will not directly absorb the whole of these, it will meet the greater part of the problem and should be of value both in terms of local trade and in aiding community development in the neighbourhood.

b)   Construction
While certain preliminary work is being put in hand forthwith, the site cannot be opened for construction until the first quarter of 1955. The construction labour force will reach a peak of 2000 men early in 1956 and continue at this level for about 15 months. The contractors no doubt will recruit as much suitable labour locally as they possibly can and will have to import the rest.

c)   Operation
The operating personnel will total about 600 of which 200

will be professional staff and 400 industrial employees. This operating force will be wanted by the end of 1957 and a few will be wanted earlier. This professional staff and about 100 of the industrial employees (skilled artisans) will have to brought from elsewhere in the atomic energy project, but it is hoped to recruit about 300 people locally. No doubt many of these will find work on the construction programme and then later transfer to factory work.

Co-operation sought from local authorities

The Atomic Energy Authority will need the close co-operation of the local authorities in carrying out the development. Their assistance will be required in connection with the provision of housing, services, schools and other facilities. The first instalment of temporary houses to accommodate constructional staff will probably be erected by the Ministry of Works, but permanent housing will be necessary for operational staff and the arrangements for erecting these will be discussed later with the local authorities.

Conclusion

a) While the fast reactor will be the first one to be put up at Dounreay, the site is being regarded as an experimental station and other reactors may be put up there.

b) There will need to be the closest consultation between the future Atomic Energy Authority and the local authorities on the practical plans to be made to deal with housing, labour supply etc. Detailed discussions will take place at a later date and there is perhaps not much point in trying to go into detail at this meeting. However, in case the authorities may wish to ask any questions, the following representatives of the atomic energy undertaking are present:-
Mr Clarke – Department of Atomic Energy
Mr Kendall – Chief Engineer fast reactor
Mr Shirlaw – Director Administration and Accounts
Mr Highton – Lands Branch, Department of Atomic Energy

c) It is hoped that from the knowledge gained by the Dounreay reactor it will be possible in 7-10 years to build other breeder reactors which will lessen the strain on the national fuel resources.

Remind the meeting once again that the proceedings are confidential."

Appendices
Appendix 4

Extract from the statement to Parliament by Sir David Eccles, Minister for works, March 1st 1954.

"I now have to tell the House that our people are ready to go ahead with a far more powerful and dramatic project. It has been decided to build a big, fast reactor of the breeder type to which the Minister of Supply referred in the House on 26th January and 16th November of last year. This plant will be constructed at Dounreay in Caithness. An enterprise of this kind requires a very large site – at least some hundreds of acres – in open country, but it must be within reach of a labour supply and the amenities of community life. It must be on the coast, for the discharge of effluent and to provide seawater for cooling. It also requires a very large supply of fresh water.

Dounreay has the further advantage that development there should make a very big contribution to the revival of the Highlands. When it is in full operation, the project is expected to provide employment for some 600 men, of whom about half will be recruited locally. My honourable friend, the member for Caithness and Sutherland, who has been so persistent in his advocacy of bringing industry to the robust part of the Kingdom he represents will, I am sure, be glad that his efforts have been rewarded with so great a prize.

I must say a word about the plant at Dounreay. For safety's sake it will be housed in a large, spherical steel shell. But even in that 'dome of discovery' – and it really will be a dome of discovery – there is a very remote possibility of a slight leakage of radioactivity should there be a failure in certain parts of the plant. The local authorities have been consulted and with their help arrangements will be made as to what should be done in this most unlikely event; and I must emphasis that it is a most unlikely event.

In an enterprise of this kind it is never certain what problems will be encountered. I think it is true to say that, in the past, problems have been solved as the construction has gone along, and maybe that will be the case here. We have every hope that this fast reactor will show the way to remarkable economies in the consumption of uranium, and will become a world famous pioneer among the plants which provide electricity in the next generation."

Appendices
Appendix 5

Safety Risk Assessments.

While the Ministerial responsibility for the project itself lay in Whitehall, political responsibility for issues that affected the community rested with the Scottish Office.

By early 1954, with the strategic decisions taken, Whitehall was beginning to hand over delivery of the project to the new Atomic Energy Authority. Mr E.J.S. Clarke, of the Department of Atomic Energy in Whitehall, told the Scottish Office that the Lord President's Office would only become involved in future if questions were referred to Ministers or infrastructure costs such as new housing exceeded expectations.

However, he was anxious that Sir Robert Russell, of the Department of Health for Scotland, understood the safety risks associated with the project when entering discussions with the AEA for the first time.

"I have one comment on your note about the preliminary meeting," Clarke wrote on March 8th, 1954. "What is said there about risk does not represent my personal views. In my opinion if the risk remains as stated to Ministers in A.E.M. (54) 2, and is not evaluated anew and diminished as a result of the technical redesign in the plant, there ought to be, well in advance of the time when the plant comes into operation, full discussions with the County authorities and a paper evacuation plan drawn up covering the 14 miles radius ought to be drawn up. I do not agree with the suggestion that all this can now be dismissed as a subject for a 'few words' with the Chief Constable. We all agreed however that the risk to Thurso was such that no plans should be made at any time in respect of evacuation from it."

A week earlier, on March 1st, Sir David Eccles had informed Parliament of the selection of Dounreay. The Privy Council had removed reference to evacuation from the draft statement, a decision accepted by Sir Robert.

Copies of the draft announcement to Parliament by Sir David Eccles went to the Treasury as well as other departments for comment. A memo from the Chancellor's Private Secretary to his counterpart at the Lord President's office read:

"The Treasury, while glad to see that the compensation point is avoided in terms, are, nevertheless, not entirely happy about the rather menacing phraseology of the last two sentences in your first paragraph. As we understand it, not only is the risk very slight but the consequences of an accident are likely to amount rather to inconvenience than to peril. Compared with many existing Government establishments, including atomic energy establishments, the proposed plant, as we understand it, involves no out of the ordinary risks.

"Would you consider some alternative phrase such as: 'The plant will be housed in a large spherical shell which will reduce to a minimum the possibility of any leakage, which could only arise in the most unlikely circumstances, could only be very slight and attended by serious or lasting consequences. The local authorities have been consulted and will co-operate in any temporary arrangements which may be necessary in the highly improbable event of their being needed'."

Appendices
Appendix 6

Planning permission was swiftly granted for Dounreay but not without a thought or two.

UKAEA's application for planning permission to erect an atomic research establishment at Dounreay in the parish of Reay was registered with Caithness County Council on November 16th, 1954. Two days later, the planning and works committee met and approved the application.

"According to the Atomic Energy Act 1954, the Dounreay plans do not really require the committee's approval but the Atomic Authority naturally wish to take the local authority along with them," said county clerk James Robertson.

Bailie W.S. Finlayson, Wick, said: "We wish them the best of luck."

"And we wish ourselves the best of luck, too," added the Rev W.G. Weir, Bruan.

A few months earlier, in July 1954, Sir Donald Perrott and C.J. Highton of the AEA travelled to Edinburgh to meet civil servants from the Scottish Office, led by Sir Robert Russell of the Health Department. The first item on the agenda was planning permission, and who should grant it.

"Mr Highton explained that there would be a lot of secret work at the station. The Authority were therefore averse to giving details of the station to the local planning authority and he suggested that the Secretary of State should issue a direction calling in the application for planning permission," the minutes state.

"He observed that the Minister had made an Order in England permitting the erection of buildings not exceeding 50ft in height, etc. The Authority would prefer to have an Order giving them authority to build anything within the site. The Official Secrets Act would apply to the station."

"Sir Robert Russell agreed that it would be possible to call in the application under Section 13 of the Town and Country Planning (Scotland) Act, 1947, and relieve the authority from giving details to the planning authority; the Department would, of course, consult the local planning authority and there would have to be agreement as to how much they should be told."

Nonetheless, the subsequent decision to submit a planning application, albeit with little of the scrutiny one might expect today, resulted in a public affirmation of the area's support for the project.

The scope of that planning permission, which effectively gave UKAEA permission to erect any facilities required under the 1954 Act, would come under severe challenge 40 years later by Highland Regional Council, as the successor body to Caithness County Council, when it sought to control the site's diversification into commercial reprocessing by arguing it was a "change of use" that required a new planning application.

Richard Cameron, director of planning at the regional council, in 1992 advised councillors: "There are no surviving docketed plans of this 1954 permission available from planning or UKAEA files. However, an industrial development certificate from the Board of Trade issued prior to the grant of planning permission related to a substantial development of 250,000 square feet of industrial building. The earliest available planning authority docketed plan dates from 1958."

Appendices
Appendix 7

The Cold War gave Dounreay's airstrip an added purpose.

In 1953, when officials at the Ministry of Works opened talks with the military about acquiring the site, those responsible for the defence of the UK did not want to lose an airfield that would be important for both US and UK aircraft with targets in the communist states.

In December 1953, the Minister of Supply gave five undertakings to the Secretary of State for Air in return for the land:

1. The Ministry would be consulted about the siting of the atomic energy buildings, including any future runway extensions.
2. The main Dounreay runway and its approaches would remain unobstructed, and full consultation must take place prior to sanctioning the construction of any buildings that might interfere with planes landing or taking off.
3. That certain existing military buildings would be left intact for use in a future war.
4. That in the event of a war, the runway and associated buildings would be immediately available for operational use, irrespective of whatever construction stage the atomic energy plant was at.
5. That the atomic energy organisation would at no future time erect buildings or take any action which would interfere with the wartime availability of the main runway, without the agreement of both the Air Ministry and the Admiralty.

The Ministry relented on one of its demands – that all activities at the atomic site should cease in the event of war. A token point in reality, perhaps, since Dounreay was one of 52 prime Soviet targets during the Cold War.

Appendices
Appendix 8

Extracts from a speech by Sir Christopher Hinton at the American industrial Conference of 1953 and its aftermath.

Sir Christopher warned that no amount of gadgets or controls could make a reactor safe unless its design was inherently so. The hazards at that time were being assessed only on the basis of calculations as no one had any practical experience of what happened when a reactor went out of control.

He added: "The magnitude of the disaster in the event of such an accident is so great that no responsible engineer or industrialist could contemplate taking the responsibility for it. It is no use to complain that the scientists are laying down rules for safety distances that are unreasonable; they are doing nothing more than stating the intensity of radiation that they think might exist at given distances from the accident. Accidents almost invariably happen to all plants and machines which break into pioneering fields; many of the early bridges collapsed, many of the early boilers blew up, and many of the early aeroplanes (and indeed the new types of aeroplanes produced today) crashed. Our trouble in the design of reactors lies primarily in the fact that engineers learn from their mistakes rather than their successes, and in the case of a nuclear reactor the penalty for failure is so great that the responsible engineer dare not risk incurring it."

Hinton suggested to his American audience that it would be worthwhile building a reactor in a remote location, purely with the intention of making it become "super-critical" to learn what happened in such conditions. Such a test, he stated, would cost no more than the trial of a single atom bomb and might yield information of tremendous value. "May I suggest to you that with all your tremendous resources of money and of technical capacity, and with the great areas of thinly populated country which you conveniently have at your disposal, this is an experiment which you might well carry out."

Sir Archibald Sinclair, the former Liberal leader, Scottish Secretary and MP for Caithness and Sutherland, raised Hinton's remarks with the Lord President, the Marquis of Salisbury, in February 1955. "I enclose herewith an extract from The Times report of Sir Christopher Hinton's speech, to which I referred in my Question. This fast breeder reactor is certainly being erected in a thinly populated – but by no means uninhabited – district; and the burgh of Thurso (population five thousand) is within less than ten miles of it. In view of the authority and weight of Sir Christopher Hinton's warning, would it not be worthwhile, before actually erecting this station – or at least before bringing it into operation – to adopt his suggestion of building a reactor in a remote district 'purely with the intention of making it become super-critical and of finding out what actually happened under those conditions'? Perhaps an alternative test has been adopted or is in preparation? If so, I should be very grateful for your assurance on this point."

The Lord President replied: "I'm afraid that in answering it I shall have to enter into technicalities to some extent because it is necessary to distinguish between two different types of hazard. A thermal reactor cooled by material such as water, which also helps to control the chain reaction, is liable to 'run away' if the circulation of the water fails, and our theoretical knowledge is not by itself sufficient to show conclusively what would then happen. This is the type of reactor to which Sir Christopher Hinton was referring in his address to the American Industrial Conference Board, and for which he suggested that a trial of the effects of a runaway was worth making.

"In fact, the US Atomic Energy Commission have since disclosed that a trial of this sort was carried out at about the time of Sir Christopher Hinton's speech, and the resulting damage was a good deal less than had been feared. This hazard does not apply to the fast breeder reactor being built at Dounreay, which is so designed that the chain reaction itself cannot in any circumstance reach explosive force. The possible danger here that has to be guarded against is a different one. Owing to the small size of the reactor core and the fact that sodium is used to carry away the heat, there is a danger of fire if the safety devices failed.

"Such a fire would evaporate some of the radioactive fission products and it is to prevent the dispersal of these that we are surrounding the reactor with a steel sphere. It is only in the extremely remote circumstance that both the reactor safety devices and the containing sphere fail together that there might be an emission of radioactivity sufficient to endanger health for an area immediately around the factory. In these circumstances we might have to evacuate temporarily the residents in this area, which would certainly not extend as far as Thurso. We naturally wish to disturb as few people as possible, and it is for this reason that we have selected a remote spot for this reactor."

Appendices
Appendix 9

Social clubs – Viewfirth and Wick.

Ormlie Lodge, an imposing mansion overlooking Thurso railway station, was acquired very early by the UKAEA in order to provide accommodation for its first group of employees, mostly senior managers, who would help with the construction of the site.

Very quickly these people formed themselves into a social grouping and named it the Ormlie Lodge Club, where pursuits such as bridge, snooker and billiards whiled away their leisure time as well as, of course, the conviviality of the lounge bar.

The Ormlie Lodge Club, which still exists today, was the embryo from which a bigger social organisation, the Dounreay Sports and Social Club (DSSC), would grow. To begin with, the DSSC met in Ormlie Lodge and held its first AGM in May 1957. However, without wanting to be a rival or undermine the Ormlie Club, the founding members felt they would only flourish when they had their own premises.

By establishing a nuclear site at Dounreay, with Thurso identified as the town to become the new home for those who would come north to be employed, the UKAEA was anxious to create a harmonious atmosphere within the incoming families and with the wider community. What better way than to establish a centre where these people could meet, socialise, and pursue their leisure interests?

On the western outskirts of Thurso stood Viewfirth House, a very elegant, stone-built house, built around 1870. It was latterly home to the Ironside family, of whom the father, the late Thomas Ironside, was the retired rector of the Miller Academy, Thurso. It had sufficient ground around it for any necessary expansion, it was adjacent to the area where UKAEA was constructing a new housing scheme for their incoming employees and, importantly, it was available. Viewfirth was very attractive in every respect and so, on February 1st 1958, the UKAEA took over ownership of Viewfirth House.

Conversion work commenced immediately, and by the following winter it was ready for the Dounreay Sports and Social Club to assume occupancy. By the time the second AGM was held in April 1958, the chairman, C.R. Tottle, who was head of reactors, was able to report that all available rooms in the club were ready for use, and that the steward's and stewardess's quarters had been completed. He also reported that there were enough funds available to make a start on the foundation and the shell of the proposed new hall.

The secretary, O.J. Booth, was equally upbeat. He advised that the club was proving very popular and already a number of leisure and recreational sections had been formed, including angling, sailing, football, cricket, hockey, tennis and bridge. But he did sound a note of warning by reminding members that it would be some time before the club was able to make money, and appealed to the various sections to be patient and moderate in their financial demands, and to make every effort to raise their own funds. It would prove to be a cautionary tale. That said, the club was well established.

Very quickly, Viewfirth, as the club became affectionately known, made itself the in-place, the place to be seen, so much so that within two years membership stood at 1700. Membership was automatically available to all UKAEA employees and their families, while non-UKAEA employees could apply for associate membership.

With the addition of new facilities, including a function room, the club was able to provide a wide range of entertainment. Dances, concerts, various stage acts and bingo evenings drew in the crowds. A number of couples chose Viewfirth as the venue for their wedding and trade union organisations also used as a meeting venue. The various individual sections also made full use of the facilities. The UKAEA's original concept that such a location would create a sense of social togetherness appeared to be bearing fruit.

Probably one of the most successful sections it helped spawn was the folk music club. During the 1970s it would make Thurso a popular destination for a host of national and international artists. Each July, over a long weekend, at various spots in the town, crowds flocked to hear the diverse acts. For a number of years the BBC recorded many of the concerts for later radio transmission. The showpiece event was Sunday afternoon on Viewfirth green – weather permitting – when all the acts came together for a farewell gig. Viewfirth was the site chosen by the Northern Nashville Country Music Club. It was responsible for taking some of the biggest names in country and western music to Caithness.

But it was not all plain sailing. One of the problems that increasingly was besetting the club was how best to cater for a varied clientele, and keep them all happy. Society was rapidly changing; people were becoming more sophisticated, their social demands increasing – and there was television. In an attempt to meet these demands the club management introduced a number of new attractions. They provided meals, particularly bar-suppers, and they engaged bands and stage acts up from the south along with other innovations. All proved popular for a while, but the novelty eventually wore off. On a few occasions, the takings at the door did not cover the costs of the entertainment. This, and a general drop-off in membership, started to have consequences for the finances of the club, which in turn started to impose its own restrictions on club activities.

There was also an ongoing problem with maintenance. The age and style of the original building, together with the extensions and alterations that had been carried out, required fairly constant attention – it all provided further aggravation for the club management.

During the 1990s, in an attempt to better deal with many of their problems, the club management attempted to buy Viewfirth from the UKAEA. Despite much discussion, the proposal didn't materialize, although UKAEA did sell what remained of its original housing stock to Pentland Housing Association, a not-for-profit group formed by tenants and residents who were opposed to the stock being sold to a private landlord.

During this period and into the new century, the picture emerges of a very hard-working group of people who formed the management committee, backed up by very loyal employees. Despite their best efforts, against a tide of falling membership and interest, coupled with an ongoing need to refurbish the fabric, replace equipment and generally re-invest, the committee faced an almost impossible task to keep the club going.

The report presented by the secretary/treasurer to the club's AGM in July 2005, said it all. Phrases like "the accounts do not make happy reading… the club is underused… fierce competition from elsewhere" and, most revealing of all, "the membership has decreased". That membership figure was now less than five hundred. The die was cast.

On the evening of March 31st, 2006, the club premises were packed, ironically to say farewell to a symbol of altruism from another age. The hopes that UKAEA harboured fifty years earlier, that such a place would bind this new community, had long been realised. It was time now to move on and hand the property back to UKAEA.

Wick Dounreay Sports and Social Club

Wick Dounreay Sports and Social Club has existed in the burgh for over forty years although it came about in a much different manner to that of Viewfirth, its Thurso counterpart.

Wick traditionally had a number of clubs, one of which was called the Seaforth Club. Clubs bearing this name existed in other areas and were born out of the camaraderie forged by people who had served in World War Two and others who had carried out their national service with the Seaforth Highlanders, the regiment most closely associated with the northern Highlands.

In the early 1960s, a group of club regulars, who were former Seaforth Highlanders, and who were among an increasing number of Wick people gaining employment at Dounreay, felt there was scope in Wick for another establishment, this time catering for families with a Dounreay connection. The foundations were laid.

Shortly afterwards, premises were acquired above the local sea cadet premises in Breadalbane Street. UKAEA helped by providing vital furniture but did not have a financial stake in the venture.

Very quickly its popularity grew, and given the limited available space, members felt they had to look for new premises that would provide scope to cater for a variety of interests and functions.

They hadn't long to wait, nor had they to look far. In the same street was located the Breadalbane Cinema, one of two cinemas in Wick. With the growing popularity of television and changing social habits, cinemas were experiencing a drop-off in attendance. The Breadalbane decided to close its doors. With the help of private finance the premises were acquired, and the members quickly set about its refurbishment.

Given the space available, the club was able to provide a number of facilities for its members, and for over 30 years provided enjoyable social amenities for its members and guests. However, in recent years, changing social habits and a dwindling membership ate away at its viability. In 2007, the shutters in this once popular venue came down for the last time.

Appendices
Appendix 10

1959 Paper by Dounreay Director Dr. Robert Hurst on the social and economic impact of Dounreay.

In February 1959, some nine months before DFR went critical, the new site director Dr Robert Hurst presented this paper to the Dounreay management committee. Even today, it is a very perceptive analysis of how Dounreay was impacting, socially and economically, both for good and evil, on the county. It also reveals, perhaps for the first time, the problems facing those responsible for managing a remote location site, given remoteness was one of the elements considered vital when the site was initially chosen. And, with great foresight, even with the site still in its infancy, Dr Hurst looked ahead to what would happen the day when the Dounreay site was no more; he was thinking in terms of what modern managers would term an 'exit strategy.'

Almost certainly, this critique, entitled "The Viability of Dounreay", if it had been made public at the time, would have proven controversial but Dr Hurst, in chronicling the problems, was wise enough to attempt to recognise their cause:-

In 1959 the AEX (Atomic Energy Executive) had laid down that the staff of Dounreay should not exceed "some 2,500". We have now reached the point where the implementation of this policy may require reshaping of the Dounreay programme to ensure that this finite number of staff are deployed on work vital to the Establishment and that other work is placed elsewhere. This could involve handing over to industry items now being undertaken at Dounreay. Important problems of organisation and lay-out, including the housing of Authority staff, require affirmation of long term policy before they can be settled. Experience has also shown that there are underlying sociological and economic questions involved in settling a large institution in so remote an area that must also have answers if this institution is to be both efficient and happy within a framework of a generally satisfied wider community.

The Present Technical Programme of D.E.R.E and Manpower Requirements

The present Dounreay programme and forecast manning requirements indicate that the figure of 2,500 will be reached in the Spring of 1962 on a basis of 1,150 non-industrials and 1,350 industrials. By 1966 the non-industrial requirement rises to 1,190 and logically calls for a similar small rise in the industrial field. Some trimming, however, may be possible, and of course in so far as industrials are found locally the Authority's position is not materially affected by marginal increments. To the Caithness authorities, however, as is discussed below, every influx into Dounreay brings difficulties in its train.

The Managerial Problem

There are four factors, each derived from the remoteness of Dounreay, which complicate the task of management. These are:-

- The distance from the various Authority headquarters and main centres of activity.
- The lack of industrial support in the Highlands and to some extent in Scotland generally.
- The remoteness from the main centres of general scientific and technical activity.
- The settlement of a new community in an outlying area.

The four factors taken together call for the absence, particularly of senior staff, from Dounreay for long periods and also for management being

closely concerned in many matters which would not come their way in larger centres of population. The general result is to keep management constantly overstretched in their endeavours to carry out the scientific tasks with which they are charged. The reverse difficulty also applies in that others concerned whether from inside or outside the Authority, find it difficult to give them the attention to Dounreay which its needs require. The risk of Dounreay not being managed in accordance with the best practice of the day and of its staff falling behind the up-to-date advancement of their various professions is high. This applies equally in such areas as Trade Unionism where the shop stewards are too remote for efficiency from their various headquarters. Although numerous ad hoc remedial actions have been taken and we can say that progress made so far has been satisfactory, there is likely to come a time when this could no longer be true. Limitation on the size of the Establishment and concentration on its really vital work are the only measures which would give confidence that the high standard of the Establishment's endeavour can be maintained. It would not follow, of course, that such limitation would apply for ever, but at least stability should be maintained for a number of years.

The Authority Community

The establishment of the Authority community in Caithness throws up a number of difficult problems which would not arise in larger centres of population. This it is necessary to set out in some detail.

The population of Caithness in 1954 (i.e. excluding the Authority influx) was about 25,000 of whom 40 per cent were concentrated in two towns, Wick (7,000) and Thurso (3,000). Agriculture and fishing were the staple industries, there being little or no manufacturing enterprise. This was reflected in education where, generally speaking, science was relatively very weak and there was an almost total absence in technical training. The county further suffered from the chronic troubles of the north of Scotland, i.e. migration due to lack of work, bad communications and lack of capital to stimulate new endeavours. Agriculture and fishing, although fairly prosperous, also tended to offer fewer opportunities since to remain competitive they were forced to intensify their methods and where possible to reduce labour. At all relevant times the unemployment figure in the county has been well above the Scottish average and hence even more above the figure for Great Britain as a whole.

Into one town and its immediate area in this county the Authority currently intends to import 1,000 married households, i.e. allowing an average of two children per family, something like 4,000 persons. There are further minor consequences importations by other authorities, e.g. by the Civil Departs, North Scotland Hydro-Electric Board etc, but these may be ignored as not being a major factor in the situation.

The Authority influx is as different in quality as in quantity in that being made up of scientists, engineers and administrators, it does not graft naturally on to the sociological formation of Caithness at any point. In addition it is 50 per cent non-Scottish and instinctively urban in its outlook.

On the other hand, broadly speaking, Dounreay can offer one job to a local man or woman for every worker it imports into Caithness. There are substantial benefits to trade in the Thurso district and the valuable stimulus that new people and new ideas can give to any community.

The Authority build-up is now about 50 per cent complete (500 houses). So far the first line arrangements made both by the Authority itself and the county have been effective. The imported and the local communities live side by side in amity. The fascination of creating a worthwhile Establishment coupled with a generous policy of material inducements and concessions has kept Authority staff morale in general high although this in not wholly true of their wives. The county authorities are fully alive to the value of Dounreay and to the intangible asset that it has put Caithness on the map. Social services and amenities have expanded, all children are being taught; a technical school is opening to carry students initially to S2 National level and later to O.N.C. level. Arrangements have been made to give further education in Aberdeen. This, however, has been the honeymoon period.

The Problem Facing the Authority

There are four reasons peculiar to Dounreay which militate against staff settling down from here. They are:-

- In perhaps the majority of cases career prospects inevitably mean transfer from Dounreay in circumstances which involve a substantial change in family life.

- The lack of urban and cultural opportunities and also of opportunities to improve oneself in one's profession. To this must be added the lack of female amenities, particularly of course, shopping.

- The deficiencies in the local education system which can only offer the standard public Scottish education which in particular gives little outlet on the scientific and technical sides. This will be greatly aggravated by the lack of opportunity for school leaving children in the local economy. In the decade 1960/70 up to 200 children annually will reach critical points in their education and their future is already a major source of concern to parents. Even those who can afford it cannot be expected to welcome the splitting up of their families. For those who cannot afford it the position is a grave one.

- Certain basic services, especially medical services, are well below urban standards. For those with health complications in their families this is another major drawback, in particular if extensive treatment is required which automatically implies evacuation to Inverness and often Glasgow or Edinburgh.

The Authority may therefore face an embarrassingly high level of very understandable requests for transfer from staff who have completed reasonable stints at Dounreay. This is likely to be coupled with a growing reluctance of staff elsewhere to take their places. Already it is proving extremely difficult to fill some posts from anywhere in the Authority or outside.

In due course difficult cases of retirement, bereavement, etc. will add to our difficulties. It is not a happy position to think one's widow could be left without the means to transfer herself elsewhere, or, alternatively, any reasonable opportunity to enjoy a satisfactory standard of life in Caithness. Since almost everyone lives in a tied house there is, in theory at least, the risk of a family being left without a roof over their heads.

The Problem of the Caithness Authorities

The crux of this problem is that while Dounreay brings a substantial measure of prosperity to the Thurso, and to some extent the Wick area, it is of no help to the rest of Caithness. Dounreay is not large enough to generate ancillary industries on its own account and there are no other local markets to assist viability. The difficulties of competing in wider markets from so remote and poorly served an area do not make setting up in Caithness a good proposition for outside firms. In fact, Dounreay creates an unbalance in the county that is unhealthy and could lead to a social difficulty of the first order. Also, to be so materially dependent on one industry cannot be regarded as economically sound.

It must also be borne in mind that local workers coming to Dounreay either lose their traditional skills or, in the case of youngsters, have never

developed them. Any recession at Dounreay therefore means the throwing out of work of persons probably incapable of finding any other employment in the area. This is another powerful argument in favour of limiting the size of Dounreay, since from this point of view it is of paramount importance only to employ staff whom we sincerely feel are likely to be needed permanently. Moreover, our industrial needs have brought a large influx of Caithness and Sutherland residents into Thurso itself. The Thurso Council recently assessed its future housing needs at 800, half directly for Dounreay employees not entitled to Authority housing. This is probably a high figure, but it emphasises how dependent on Dounreay the town is becoming. It should also be noted that this is transference of a burden from the Authority to the town in that in 1956 the Authority forecast building 1300 houses on the assumption that non-craft industrials would have to be imported.

It is clear that the establishment of Dounreay has placed a severe strain on Caithness. Public utility services in particular are stretched to their utmost without there being sufficient justification for any worthwhile provision of new facilities. It is also certain that without substantial outside help the local authorities cannot hope to take the necessary measures in the fields of sociology, education and industrial development which the relatively sophisticated Dounreay community would regard as necessary to the reasonable standard of living. On the other hand, without such measures it would be most unwise to assume that Dounreay can be kept either scientifically sound, or in general human terms, happy.

Public opinion in the county is by no means wholly favourable to Dounreay. At the beginning there were high hopes, much stimulated by the level of construction activity, that the Establishment was the answer to the unemployment problem and would act as a focus for future industrial development. The disappointment of these hopes has led inevitably to some concentration on our failings, e.g. that lack of information on our build-up which has led to the new Thurso High School being too small on the day it opened and our difficulty at various points in accepting the Caithness way of life. Current rating levels are attributed to our demands. The growing importance of Thurso is by no means generally palatable especially to the county town, Wick, which sees itself losing in an old traditional rivalry. In Thurso itself many people fear being swamped by the new community to the derangement of their own lives.

Conclusion

There is an old Chinese proverb that he who rides on a tiger can never dismount, and this is the position of the Authority over Dounreay. Scientifically, the Establishment must be kept to the highest level. This can only be done if the social and economic infrastructure are sound. In these fields the Authority are nearly in the position of such concerns as Lever Bros., in their African development and elsewhere. While it is, of course, the responsibility of other Authorities to promote the prosperity of Caithness, their position is peculiarly difficult, and if the UKAEA does take a very positive hand in these things it is likely that the investment in Dounreay may show a very poor return.

Recommendations

- The policy of restricting Dounreay to a ceiling figure of 2,500 should stand and any necessary reshaping of the technical programme be put in hand.

- Authority policy should be to reduce the proportion of imported staff as low as possible by increasing the training facilities available for the local population. In particular the aim should be to eliminate the outside recruiting of all industrials and save for professional staff, all basic non-industrial (i.e. Assistants Scientific, A.E.O's, Clerical Assistants and Clerical Officers, etc)

- In recruiting professional or supervisory grades, preference should be given to Scots or Scottish affiliates who are more likely to find local conditions congenial and to settle in as full members of the community. The urban Lowland Scot may however be as bad a risk as his Southern counterparts. Relations should be developed with Scottish University and schools.

- These relations should extend to the provision of places in Universities and schools for Authority children, in the arts equally with science, to ensure as far as possible parents are not forced to look for education outside Scotland.

- The Authority should be prepared to export any ex-Authority employees or family who cannot reasonably make his or their own way in Caithness.

- It should be urged on the Scottish Office and, if necessary, elsewhere, in conjunction with the county, that Caithness has a serious social problem and at the same time an opportunity. It might even be appropriate to declare the county a special Development Area to open the way for the one essential adjunct – capital.

- The Authority should be prepared to give work to incoming industry even at a temporary cost of high price and relatively low efficiency to assist firms to establish themselves. Technical help should be given readily and without charge.

- Preference should be reasonably given to local sources of supply in e.g. the replacement of vehicles and other items where the product is in any case standard, even where quoted prices are not strictly competitive.

- In the same way as the Authority has offered to help the new Technical School in Thurso by providing staff, it should be prepared to help any other similar development in the county, even if no immediate benefit to Dounreay can be predicted.

- Similarly, the Authority should be prepared to participate in an advisory capacity in the promotion of any undertaking not of direct application to Dounreay but where the attitude of the Authority community may be an important factor in deciding a line of progress.

- The existing policy of giving local bodies assistance in kind should be generously interpreted.

These measures should be communicated to the County Council and Thurso Town Council (a Planning Authority in its own right) who should be urged to take concomitant steps on their own behalf.

Appendices
Appendix 11

Early difficulties with DFR.

Apart from problems with contamination of the coolant, there were other troubles that dogged the start up of DFR. When an initial attempt was made to raise the control rod carriages, six out of the 12 remained firmly wedged in place. By using the viewing devices, sludge was observed to have accrued and to be affecting the mechanics of the operation. The electromagnetic currents had to be increased to provide extra torque to free the jammed rods. A modification was undertaken on the control rod operating mechanism bearing moving it to a position whence it was submerged at all times and this avoided the accrual of impurities into the bearing as it no longer broke the surface of the coolant.

The first sign of the problem caused by the entrapment of gas bubbles occurred during an early physics experiment when the reactor was being run at low power. A reactivity change happened when the primary coolant flow rate was increased. It had also been observed that when the coolant was running at full flow rate, the level in the reactor was about 600mm higher than normal and that the level in the expansion tanks was high also. It was swiftly established that relatively large quantities of gas were being entrained.

Additional instrumentation was installed mainly for the observation and measurement of coolant levels. It was discovered that many of the by-pass circuits were blocked between the cold traps and expansion tanks with the flow well above 70% in the main circuit but with no flow in the by-pass loop. The pressure differential had been sufficient to suck all the coolant from the expansion tanks and thus encourage the entrainment of the gas.

The problem was related to the design of the control rod and thermocouple systems. Isolating the vertical tube from the blanket gas eliminated the control rod source of entrainment and, in the case of the thermocouples, slots were cut in the tops of the tubes. These modifications took some six months to complete. It was possible to work on only one control rod or thermocouple at any time and, given the twelve control rods and six thermocouples, work continued round the clock.

With the main coolant finally cleaned and the by-pass loops clear, the expansion tanks no longer emptied and this source of entrainment was removed. The control rod and thermocouple tube modifications eliminated the other two sources and all 24 circuits subsequently behaved more in accordance with their design specification expectations.

Appendices
Appendix 12

This is the text of a paper presented to the World Congress of Public Relations in Venice, May 24 – 27 1961.
It was revised in 1963 by Donald Carmichael, General Secretary, UKAEA, Dounreay.

The paper was entitled "Nuclear Fission and Social Fusion."

During the last eight years, the United Kingdom Atomic Energy Authority has built and brought into operation a large experimental reactor establishment at Dounreay in the county of Caithness, in the extreme north of Scotland. This paper gives some account of the Authority's efforts to establish and maintain good relations with the local community.

The local community

Caithness is a rough triangle of brown moors, blue lochs and fertile farms, bounded on two sides by the sea and on the thirds by a ridge of barren hills. Its geographical position, its inaccessibility except by sea, its history and its limited natural resources have combined over the centuries to produce a robust, closely knit, self-reliant community, independent to the point of being insular in its outlook, but shrewd, hard-working and hospitable. It was not until 1811 that the first road came into the county, and even today, although there is an air service, there are only two roads and one railway giving access to the south. To travel overland to Edinburgh takes 10 hours and to London 20. Thus Caithness still retains much of its remoteness and its people many of the qualities which that remoteness has engendered.

In 1900 the population of Caithness was 36,000; by 1950 it had fallen to 23,000 of which 40 per cent were concentrated in two towns – Wick (6,500) and Thurso (3,200). This decline has been coupled during recent years with an unemployment figure well above the Scottish average. Agriculture was flourishing, but the fishing industry had contracted, there was little or no manufacturing enterprise and no apparent prospect of significant development in that or any other field. Then on March 1, 1954, it was announced in the House of Commons that British scientists and engineers were ready to go ahead with a "powerful and dramatic project….the construction of a big test reactor of the breeder type", and that this reactor was to be built at Dounreay.

The local presentation of the project

Caithness County Council had been consulted before this announcement was made, but the local people were wondering what lay behind it and how their way of life would be affected. Sir Christopher Hinton, at that time Managing Director of the Industrial Group of the Authority and Member for Engineering and Production, answered both these questions in Thurso Town Hall early in January 1955, within the context of a lecture on the peaceful uses of atomic energy. Dounreay had been chosen in preference to other possible sites because it best fulfilled an unusual set of physical and geographical requirements. Of these, one of the most important was that it should be in a remote and sparsely populated area. There was an element of risk inseparable from the development of a fast breeder reactor. Every conceivable precaution would be taken, and the whole process contained in a steel sphere, but if anything should go wrong, radioactive contamination might occur in a limited zone and in an extreme case it might be necessary temporarily to evacuate those living near the reactor. In that unlikely event, the smaller the number of people inconvenienced the better.

The development at Dounreay would bring many material benefits to Caithness, and although the Authority would to some extent be changing the character of the district, these changes would be carried out as considerately as possible.

This lecture was given national press coverage, but the most gratifying comment was in a local newspaper: "While the people do not exclude the possibility of risks, they accept this great project in their midst with a true spirit of faith in the redevelopment and rehabilitation which has for so long eluded them. At the same time, Sir Christopher Hinton's special visit to reassure those chiefly concerned and the public generally on the question of safety is much appreciated. Whatever anxiety was felt has been largely removed by his frank appraisal of the position. By taking the people into his confidence, he showed great wisdom."

The establishment of Dounreay

Work on site began in March 1955 and the establishment was complete in all major respects by the end of 1958. It cost £25 million to build and nearly 3,000 men (half of them local) were engaged on its construction. By siting it on a disused airfield the Authority caused the least possible disturbance to agriculture, and some 800 acres of additional land which the Authority wished to control in the immediate neighbourhood was acquired without the irritation and publicity of compulsory purchase. This land has been re-let to its former owners, and in a discriminating agricultural community the Authority now enjoys the reputation of being a good landlord. Sunday working, essential for the speedy completion of the project, was justified in the eyes of all save a strict Calvinistic minority, and in general the transient, but very real social and economic disturbance inseparable from a big construction project was kept well within bounds.

Various lectures and exhibitions were arranged by the Authority to foster local investment in atomic energy during the construction of the Establishment. In May 1957 a Press Day and an Open day were held. At the former, interests as far apart at the Caithness Courier and Tass were represented; on the latter 6,500 local people were shown round the partially completed site.

The Establishment's present strength is nearly 2,400. Of those, about 1,000 are imported key men – scientists, engineers, craftsmen and administrators – of whom only half are Scottish. The remainder are English, with a strong seasoning of Welsh and a few Irish. Most of them come from urban or industrial areas, and they thus form a heterogeneous group widely different from the local people in their antecedents and outlook. The task of settling them and their families in Caithness was only one of a number of social problems which the remoteness of the area and the rapidity of the development at Dounreay brought prominently into the field of local relations. These problems were briefly, housing, education, public services and utilities, social amenities, employment and the grafting of the new group on to the sociological structure of Caithness.

Social expansion in Caithness

To formulate policy and to keep the problems under review, the Authority held a series of meetings, dating back to May 1954, with Caithness County Council and Thurso Burgh Council. Government Departments were also represented and the Chair was taken, whenever possible, by Sir Donald Perrott, at that time Member of the Authority for Finance and Administration. The results of this joint planning and of the new stimulus to private endeavour are most evident in the town of Thurso, where most of the Authority's imported staff are accommodated. Thurso is now three times as big as it was seven years ago. 1,500 new houses have been built – 1,000 by the Authority and most of the remainder by the Burgh, with some special assistance from the public funds. Old shops have expanded;

new shops have appeared. The Authority has built two hostels – one for young imported staff and another for locally recruited lads under training as apprentices at Dounreay. It has provided playing fields and a recreation club, primarily for Dounreay, but with associate membership for native Thursonians. The Town Council has plans for more playing fields and a new Town Hall. The Roman Catholics have built an elegant church in what used to be a stronghold of Presbyterianism. A new High School has replaced the old Miller Academy, where a rigorous but narrow discipline has produced many scholars but few scientists; and a Technical College, the first of its kind north of Aberdeen, was opened four years ago on the fringe of the town.

The local people are generally appreciative of what Dounreay has brought to Caithness – more jobs (1,200 of them permanent ones at Dounreay, where, other things being equal, preference is given to local applicants), more opportunities for young people, more money, more business, a broader system of education, better social services, the stimulus of new people with new ideas and the intangible asset of being put more prominently on the map. They gave an almost unqualified welcome to the new-comers – the "atomics" for their part have settled down with a minimum of friction and are adjusting themselves positively and intelligently to their new physical and social environment. There is nothing forced or self conscious in the group relationship, and for that reason – if for no other – it seems likely to endure.

The population of Caithness is now 27,500. The future of this growing community will depend mainly on employment, particularly employment for young people. Dounreay has already given jobs to many young people, both local and "atomic". The new emphasis on science in the schools and the training at the Technical College will open the door to many more. But Dounreay will not be able to take them all. Some will have to find other jobs in the county, or, as in the past, go elsewhere. The Authority has therefore already taken measures to provide special outlets for them by setting up its Central Superannuation Office in Thurso and by starting a clerical and secretarial training scheme for school-leavers in conjunction with Thurso Technical College. In addition, every effort is being made, in collaboration with the County Council, to attract other industries to Caithness, and so achieve a balanced economy.

The outcome, however, might well have been different if other less obvious conditions essential for the friendly and profitable co-operation of social groups had not been fulfilled. A closer analysis of the facts might therefore make a significant contribution to the development of the "science of man" which David Hume foresaw 200 years ago – a science in which "we must glean up our experiments from a cautious observation of human life, and take them as they appear in the common course of the world, by men's behaviour in company, in affairs and in their pleasures. When experiments of this kind are judiciously collected and compared, we may hope to establish on them a science which will not be inferior in certainty, and will be much superior in utility, to any other of human comprehension."

Summary

During the last eight years the United Kingdom Atomic Energy Authority has built and commissioned an experimental reactor establishment at Dounreay, in Caithness, in the extreme north of Scotland. The Establishment, of which the focal point is the Fast Breeder Reactor, (Britain's most advanced large-scale experiment in the industrial application of atomic energy) now employs 2,400 people, of whom over 1,000 are key men imported with their families from urban England and the industrial south of Scotland.

The impact of this rapid and unique development on a remote agricultural and fishing community of 23,000 souls set the Authority some unusual problems in the field of local relations. Of these, the more important were:-

- the initial local presentation of a project to which there was attached a slight, but admitted, element of radioactive risk.
- the containment, within reasonable limits, of the disturbance inseparable from a costly and urgent construction programme.
- the settling of the Authority's imported staff and their families in their new environment, and the reinforcement, in construction with both central and local government, of all basic services to meet the joint needs of the expanding community.
- the grafting of the new group on to the old, with a view to ultimate fusion.
- the provision of a sound economic future for the growing community.

All these problems have been, or are being, resolved. This success is seen to be due mainly to:-

- the frank and well-timed release of information by the Authority both to the public and local government.
- The friendly realism of the local people and the co-operation of the local authorities.
- the attitude of the Authority's imported staff to their new environment.
- the Authority's personal contacts in a community which in all its relationships has been accustomed to deal with individuals rather than with an amorphous body.
- the Authority's clear-cut conception of its social obligations and in particular its willingness to take positive action on any problems created wholly or partially by the establishment of Dounreay.

The outcome, however, might well have been different if other less obvious conditions essential for the friendly and profitable co-operation of social groups had not been fulfilled. A closer analysis is therefore proposed of this small but well-defined experiment in sociology.

Appendices
Appendix 13

Dounreay and the community.

Throughout its lifetime at Dounreay, the UKAEA has been well aware of its social obligations to the local community and has met that obligation either by working with the community directly or by encouraging staff to be involved in and assist in the various groups of the area. This outgoing, not to say altruistic policy, was inherent in Dounreay from the start and speaks well of its early founders and those who have subsequently taken the responsibilities upon themselves.

Over the years many individual organisations, various projects and the community in general have benefited. Dounreay's assistance comes in many ways. Through a fund provided by the Nuclear Decommissioning Authority and administered by Dounreay (currently valued at £20,000) donations have been disbursed to a wide range of groups; redundant equipment, for example computers, printers, and fax machines has been frequently donated to voluntary organisations and over the years staff have been given time off to help out with community projects; for example, staff have helped create pathways in Dunnet Forest and along the Thurso river in conjunction with the British Conservation Trust Volunteers.

The engineering craft apprentices have a long tradition of community involvement. Many decorated floats, with amusing themes, for various gala processions, were put together in the apprentice training workshop. A number of voluntary organisations also benefited from their sweat and toil, be it in terms of a direct input, or through donations from fund-raising events. The administration trainees have also been very active over the years in raising money for worthy causes including, on one occasion, "kidnapping" a well-known member of staff and demanding a ransom from his colleagues to ensure his release.

One of the largest donations made to a community group was a one-off windfall of £50,000 made to the Pulteneytown Peoples Project, a community regeneration project in Wick. In handing this sum over in the year that Dounreay celebrated its 50th birthday, Norman Harrison, the Dounreay director, said that this built upon UKAEA's long tradition of community involvement and would help regenerate one of the needier areas of the community. Of equal value to the community were the people with particular skills and interests who passed them on in their spare time, especially to the young. People who encouraged swimming, athletics, football and other pursuits through organisations like the Guides, the Scouts, the Boys Brigade and youth clubs.

And Dounreay staff can also be found in voluntary front-line services like mountain rescue teams, the Red Cross and the volunteer fire brigades. The value of Dounreay to the area has always been measured, and rightly so, in terms of what it provides in employment and revenue, but equally important to the Caithness world is a strong sense of community responsibility that Dounreay continues to shoulder.

Appendices
Appendix 14

The work of the MTR fuel fabrication plant.

The materials test reactor fuel fabrication plant was the first of the so-called Dounreay chemical plants to be completed and put into operation. The manufacture of fuel elements was an essential component in what was called the E443 reactor programme, which dated back to the earliest days of the UKAEA and may have predated its formation in 1954. The initial E443 programme was for three reactors in the UK, namely, in order of completion, DIDO, PLUTO and DMTR. A further three reactors in overseas locations, Denmark, Germany and Australia were being considered, and indeed were subsequently built.

Whilst the E443 project was very much Harwell (Research Group) based, the manufacture and reprocessing of the irradiated fuel was put into the hands of the UKAEA Industrial Group, based at Risley and responsible for building all the UKAEA's production facilities, including Capenhurst, Springfields, Windscale and Dounreay. The main industrial collaborator at this time was ICI Metals Division, notable producers and fabricators in non-ferrous metals. The specification for the plant was complete in March 1955 so that the design and construction could proceed to meet the February 1957 completion date.

The centre of the building housed a block which contained the glove boxes, plant etc. Glove box operations were carried out from the north operating corridor. The highly enriched uranium (HEU) was delivered in the form of 2.5Kg uranium metal billets produced in an adjacent building. A total of eight glove boxes were provided originally. These were used for receipt of raw materials, storage of fissile material, breakdown of casts, a cropping machine, a weighing machine, furnaces, moulds and casting. The main feature of the rest of the line was the provision of three rolling mills.

The facility was substantially complete by the end of 1956 and training of operators commenced early in 1957. As was to prove to be the case on many occasions, manufacture of complete elements was delayed by the lack of various aluminium element components. However, steady progress was made and 21elements were reported as completed in March 1957. By April, the total had risen to 40 complete elements with an additional 15 fuel element boxes.

The MTR fuel fabrication plant supplied all of the fuel elements used in the DIDO and PLUTO reactors at Harwell from 1957 until their closure in 1990. It also provided fuel for a variety of customers at home and abroad, including the Merlin and Herald reactors, universities, Denmark, Germany, South Africa, India, Belgium, Australia and Holland.

When the Harwell reactors closed, the plant was still manufacturing fuel elements for the two DIDO type reactors in Germany and Australia but there was insufficient demand for fuel elements to warrant keeping it open. The decision was therefore taken to invest in the plant with the design, manufacture and installation of a new production line that enabled dispersed-type, or powdered-type, fuel to be manufactured. With the successful development of the manufacturing and inspection techniques for powdered fuel, UKAEA was able to secure contracts for the supply of fuel elements to two more materials test reactors, one in Holland and one in Belgium, that allowed the plant to continue operation until 2004. Molybdenum targets were also manufactured using the same techniques that are used for powdered fuel manufacture. These are small flat, aluminium clad plates that contain a small quantity of uranium-235. When the plates are placed within the neutron flux of a reactor, the neutrons cause fission of the uranium with the formation of fission products. One of these fission products is technetium 99 that decays to form molybdenum 99. Both Te99 and Mo99 have half lives and energies that make Mo99 suitable for use as a medical tracer and is used in the diagnosis of certain types of cancer. Several thousand of these target plates were manufactured in the fabrication plant and supplied to the MTR at Petten in Holland from the late 1990s, creating enough nuclear medicine for approximately 10 million diagnoses.

Perhaps the most remarkable fact about the MTR fuel fabrication plant was the speed with which the process was established in 1957. It continued steadily although not without threats in the early 1960s to close it down to make room for PFR fuel development. In this period there was also a serious proposal to transfer the process to Springfields. When it finally ceased production in March 2004, the last of the nuclear operations at Dounreay to come to an end, the fabrication plant moved immediately into decommissioning.

Appendices
Appendix 15

Developing techniques for examining fuel.

The examination and reprocessing of the uranium fuel from DFR and DMTR and then the plutonium fuel from PFR meant that techniques for inspection, sampling, separation, analysis and radioactive counting had to be developed by the metallurgists and chemists in the hot cells and laboratories within the Fuel Cycle Area.

Throughout the 1960s, 1970s and 1980s the Dounreay scientists were always at the cutting edge of technology and often led the world in their particular field. The instruments were always of the best and these were often developed even further to make the facilities the finest in the world. This was particularly true of those tools used for the measurements concerning plutonium and its fission products.

Two important chemical analytical methods were pioneered at Dounreay and both have now been adopted as the international standard for fuel accountancy. These are the Davies/Gray method for uranium determination (ISO 7097) and the MacDonald/Savage method for plutonium determination (ISO 8298).

In the early 1960s Bill Davies and W. Gray elaborated a chemical method for accurately determining the mass of uranium in solutions of dissolved fuel. The great advantages were that this method was highly tolerant to the level of fission products in the solution and it was compatible with the wide range of uranium metal fuels. Others have since improved the method but the basics of it remain the same.

With the advent of PFR and plutonium fuels in the mid 1970s, Dave Savage and Alex MacDonald developed a chemical titration method for accurately determining the mass of plutonium in solutions of dissolved fuel. This was more problematic determination than that for uranium as the fuel had a much higher burn-up (i.e. percentage of fuel used up was greater and hence more fission products were left over) and the dissolved solutions had very high levels of alpha radiation. This meant that the method had to be permit for remote handling in high active cells. The International Atomic Energy Agency (IAEA) sent many international chemists to Dounreay to learn the method and the chemistry was often described as "elegant" by these scientists.

The metallurgists developed remote optical examination techniques for irradiated fuel inspections using electron microscopy and x-ray diffraction techniques amongst others. They were the first to confirm the extent of neutron induced void swelling and irradiation induced creep of stainless steels within a fast breeder reactor.

Dounreay was also at the forefront of world technology in the following specialist areas:-

- Gamma and alpha spectrometry – instrumentation and computer software development for measuring many scores of radionuclides
- Thermal ionisation mass spectrometry (TIMS) – detection of individual atoms to an accuracy of three decimal places of a mass unit.
- Plutonium and uranium detection in liquids – automated measuring systems including on-line fibre-optic spectrophotometry
- Non destructive assay – hands free uranium and plutonium measurement in waste containers
- Separation of plutonium, uranium and fission products – clarification equipment and liquid-liquid extraction contactors for future generation reprocessing plants

There were hundreds of scientists involved in the above pioneering work, too many to mention, but who all contributed to the advancement of science.

Appendices
Appendix 16

Summary, "The Dounreay Rundown – Impacts and Alternatives", by PIEDA for the Highlands and Islands Development Board, April 1989.

This report measures the impacts upon, and examines the alternatives for, the Caithness economy following the Parkinson announcement in July 1988 that Government funding for the nuclear fast reactor programme would be reduced.

The implications of the Parkinson announcement are that employment at Dounreay will fall from 2110 at July 1988 to 530 in 1997, unless alternative activities are developed on site. While this is a substantial reduction in local employment, the rundown has been deliberately phased over a long period. The Government has accepted a responsibility to ensure the long-term prosperity of Caithness and help identify new sources of employment.

Dounreay Nuclear Establishment began operations in 1958. Over the intervening years, the plant has been integrated into the local economy. Some 96 per cent of the workforce are resident in Caithness, with high concentrations in Thurso and Wick. DNE accounted for approximately 18 per cent of Caithness employment in 1988 and injected around £24 million into the local economy during that year.

If the rundown at DNE was not offset by alternative employment creation, then total employment losses would eventually amount to 2440 jobs with an annual income loss of £32.5m. This would result in a substantial increase in unemployment and/or heavy out-migration.

In addition to these impacts there would be adverse social consequences affecting the social and economic infrastructure, especially in housing, education and health.

The study considers the impacts of major closures in remote areas in other countries. The impact of the DNE rundown will be significantly greater than the case studies examined. Some overseas attempts to offset major redundancies have involved continuing operating subsidies which would be less acceptable in a UK context.

In areas of the Highlands and Islands affected by other major rundowns (Corpach and Invergordon) there has been some tendency for unemployment to revert to the average Highland level over a period of years. The scale of the DNE rundown is, however, much more substantial. We do not believe that the creation of an enterprise zone would be an effective response.

We recommend that Highlands and Islands Development Board and the Government should pursue actively policies to create alternative employment in Caithness and summarise below some of the development opportunities which should be considered.

Employment will continue to fall in agriculture and there is little scope for expansion of the local fishing fleet. There may be some possibility of increased fish processing but forestry offers the major opportunity for increased employment in the primary industries.

The rundown announcement has already affected the construction sector, and a protracted period of difficulty will occur, unless offset by new public sector investment. There are some opportunities for modest employment growth, both in this sector and in peat and quarrying where improvements in the transport infrastructure would be of benefit.

In the manufacturing sector there are a number of companies with good expansion prospects, and existing skills offer an opportunity to attract new inward investment projects. Companies dependent on local demand (particularly in the service sector) will be severely affected by the rundown.

Recent and anticipated tourism developments in Caithness will improve the area's attractiveness. This should be strengthened by improved self-catering accommodation and realignment of marketing policy to take advantage of the new ferry services to Orkney. We recommend that the HIDB should pursue its policy of promoting the 'A9 trail' and developing other visitor attractions.

It will be extremely difficult to offset the impact of the rundown unless major new employment opportunities can be created at DNE itself. These fall into two major categories – non-nuclear and nuclear.

As regards non-nuclear opportunities, the time-frame for development is relatively short and does not extend beyond the anticipated shutdown of the PFR in 1994. We consider that it may be difficult to compete on a commercial basis in the generation of electricity, but there may be an opportunity for a significant expansion of commercial technical services. The HIDB should pursue both options with DNE as a matter of urgency.

The nuclear options are difficult to forecast with any precision. A key decision appears to be that relating to the possible Nirex repository, which may make it more likely that other activities involving nuclear waste reprocessing and disposal are located in Caithness. A number of these options would create substantial employment, both during the construction and operating phases.

We believe that Caithness might be a suitable location for 'back office' public and private sector office employment. The former are particularly important in view of the present review of civil service activities, but HIDB should also investigate the opportunities for mobile projects in the private sector. Implementation of an upgraded telecommunications network may be necessary to realise any opportunities.

Since the fundamental objective must be to create new employment in 'export base' activities, the further upgrading of the A9, the upgrading of Scrabster Harbour, improvements at Wick Airport and investment in telecommunications are recommended. Improvements in business support are required. These should include enterprise training for DNE employees seeking to start up in business and also the provision of training programmes focussed on youth.

The HIDB should review its existing budget priorities to give greater emphasis to Caithness. Central government should also be prepared to review the level of the HIDB's budget, as it appears probable that the cost of job creation in Caithness will rise appreciably. It is recommended that assisted area status be conferred on Caithness should employment in the area continue to fall, even although the unemployment rate (perhaps due to out migration) remains below current criteria for assisted area designation. The development option should be pursued with determination by the Government and all its agencies.

Appendices
Appendix 17

Prospectus for the sale of AEA Technology housing, Thurso, issued by Finlayson Hughes, chartered surveyors, circa 1992.

The establishment of Dounreay in the mid-1950s created a substantial increase in population for the Thurso area and, to provide accommodation for staff at Dounreay from outwith the area, 1007 houses and flats were constructed, mainly in Thurso, between 1955 and 1963. In addition, infrastructure and amenities such as two primary schools, high school and technical college were also built and the population of Thurso had leapt from 3249 in 1951 to 8037 in 1961.

Although, in its early days it was necessary for AEA to build houses of a suitable standard as a recruitment and retention incentive, that need no longer exists because the local infrastructure is capable of supporting Dounreay without the need for a large private holding of houses.

AEA Technology is treated in law as a private landlord and its tenants therefore do not have a right to buy. However, over the years sales of houses have taken place largely along the lines of the Government's "right to buy" scheme with tenants being offered a substantial discount. The housing stock on Pennyland and Mount Vernon estates in Thurso managed by AEA Technology has therefore reduced over the years to the current situation where there is now a large number of owner-occupied properties on both estates creating a stable population and the appearance and atmosphere more of a private estate than is the typical case with much local authority housing.

The most recent offer to the tenants giving them the right to buy their houses has now closed and no more applications are being accepted. There are therefore currently 351 houses and flats still in AEA Technology ownership with 20 sales to tenants being processed at the present time. It is anticipated that all the sales will go through to completion. It should also be noted that, since the right to apply to purchase was withdrawn, a substantial number of additional enquiries have been received from tenants wishing to buy their houses and there is thought to be scope for a purchaser of the housing stock to continue sales to tenants.

AEA Technology are offering for sale the 351 houses still remaining in their ownership together with 474 garages and the areas of land associated with the housing and garages as shown on the plan in the appendix. Those houses currently "under offer" to the tenants which do not proceed to completion will be added into the sale. The houses and garages produce a substantial income, detailed later in the brochure, producing a good return in addition to the possibility of capital produced by the sales to tenants in the future.

Both Mount Vernon and Pennyland estates are within three quarters of a mile of the town centre served by local bus services. Pennyland estate has three children's play areas, two large playing fields, a privately-owned general grocery store, and the Mount Vernon estate has a children's play area, playing field and swimming pool nearby. Of the 351 houses for sale, 14 are on the Mount Vernon estate together with 23 garages, the remainder being in Pennyland.

Prospective purchasers of the housing block will no doubt be aware that a progressive reduction in funding for Dounreay was announced in 1988. Articles in newspapers and magazines as well as on the television have produced the impression that the Dounreay facility will be completely closed down by the turn of the century providing little or no employment.

However, this bears no relation to AEA Technology's present plans for Dounreay. Although the workforce has dropped from 2200 in 1988 to around 1650 currently, this workforce will primarily be engaged in fuel services (nuclear fuel fabrication, processing and reprocessing). decommissioning, some diversification and associated services activities. Turnover is expected to stabilise at around £80 million per annum over the next decade contributing about £30 million to the local economy each year.

It is therefore expected that there will be considerable continuing demand for rented housing from those working at Dounreay and it is therefore highly likely that the present high occupancy rate of the housing will continue and that, whilst Dounreay's influence on the economy will be reduced from its peak it will still be a very substantial employer and contributor to the local economy for many years to come.

Appendices
Appendix 18

The Radioactive Waste Management Advisory Committee's (RWMAC) Advice to Ministers on Radioactive Waste Management Issues at UKAEA Dounreay, January 1999.

The role of Dounreay, and public perceptions of it, have changed markedly over the last 40 years. There is evidence that activities in the early years, essentially those of research into fast breeder reactor technology, were regarded as uncontroversial and were relatively popular, although this statement needs to be qualified by the fact that many operations were carried out secretively, reflecting the cold war conditions under which much of the nuclear industry worked at the time. There may have been reasonable local knowledge of operations at Dounreay, but little meaningful publicity about them was officially given out.

UKAEA was perceived as a good employer, providing training and investment in the local economy. The Authority built 1200 houses for its workers in Thurso and supported a range of facilities, including a college. Thurso trebled in population in the 10 years after the mid-1950s, reaching 10,000 at its peak.

The RWMAC believes that the Government's decision in 1988 to bring the fast breeder programme to an end was an important turning point. The abandonment of development work appears to have marked a shift in the institutional culture of the plant corresponding to the change in its operational role. The earlier period of confident belief in experimental technology was succeeded by a more defensive, and in recent years embattled, attitude as the rundown of operations has proceeded.

In more recent years, there has been an increasing public focus on the plant's activities, just as the nuclear industry as a whole has been opened up to more public scrutiny. At Dounreay, the process appears to have been a difficult one. The secrecy associated with the plant's origins has gradually been replaced by a stated "open and honest" policy, but the public image of the plant has been undermined by a series of accidents, incidents and revelations about mistakes in past waste management activities.

It is difficult to avoid the conclusion that fast reactor research was pursued with little thought as to how the resulting radioactive wastes were to be managed. In essence, the standards of radioactive waste management achieved fell short of reasonable expectations of the time, let alone those required today. It is equally difficult wholly to exculpate the governmental and regulatory authorities in existence at the time, as well as the UKAEA managers themselves, from sharing in responsibility. There is a legacy of poor practices from the past which are still causing problems today and which amount to a burden on the present Dounreay management, particularly in its relationship with some elements of the local and regional communities.

In practice, the more vociferous critical scrutiny originated outside the immediate area. There is a substantial view that this may have originated in two different, although associated, sets of events. In 1989, Nirex announced that it was considering Dounreay for a possible site for the UK's deep radioactive waste repository. It seems that Dounreay management were enthusiastic about the proposal but some plant workers and local people were much less supportive. (A referendum organised by the Electoral Reform Society in 1989, on behalf of Caithness District Council, found that, among the council electorate, opponents of deep disposal at Dounreay outnumbered supporters by 3:1. The question was "Are you in favour of a Nirex deep level repository being built in Caithness?" In a 58 per cent turnout, 74 per cent voted no and 26 per cent voted yes.)

Then, in 1993, there was a press campaign to publicise the condition of LLW pit 6. Councillors and others who were shown the pits and other areas gained a negative impression of some aspects of radioactive waste management at the plant. The Nirex proposal and the pit 6 issue gave credence to an emerging view that Dounreay management had an insufficient grasp on some key issues of radioactive waste management and added impetus to the campaign against the plant. During the early 1990s, a much more sceptical view arose. This is particularly developed in surrounding areas, such as the Highlands and Western Isles and also the Orkneys and Shetlands (which have many traditional ties to anti-nuclear Norway). Opinion in Caithness itself was divided.

The role of Dounreay within the local community has also changed. For most of its history, Dounreay has been seen, rightly or wrongly, as something of a "closed shop", favouring local businesses and local workers. The abandonment of fast breeder work and the adoption of a wider range of commercial activities, including the reprocessing of foreign fuel, seems to have begun the process by which Dounreay is viewed less and less as a "local" operation. Nevertheless, the fact that the plant is very likely to continue to carry out nuclear operations, of one sort or another, for several decades remains a key factor in its relationship with the local communities. Its significance for the local economy should not be underestimated.

UKAEA's standing has also been affected by the processes of privatisation and contractorisation which have occurred at the plant. These seem together to have had two effects. There is uncertainty and insecurity among some of the workforce which will have affected morale. On the other hand, a new breed of management has been introduced, largely via the management support contract, which is little connected to the previous culture. The management is providing a more vigorous focus on the new core activities of long-term decommissioning and waste management activities at the plant.

At present, there is relatively little public debate about decommissioning and waste management at Dounreay. These are requirements, not options, for the site in the future. Current opinion is polarised however about reprocessing in the context of the strategic future of Dounreay. In detail, the debate is largely centred around whether the PFR reprocessing plant irradiated fuel dissolver should be replaced.

Supporters of reprocessing believe that its cessation would lead to a loss of expertise similar to that which occurred at the end of the fast breeder programme. (In the late 1980s, some of the professional dedication associated with ground-breaking research work, the "spirit of Dounreay", appears to have been lost as the expertise assembled at the plant was dispersed.) It is also argued that the best option for Dounreay PFR fuel is that it is managed at the point of arising.

Beyond questions about the extent of investment in the Fuel Cycle Area, there is a major division of opinion on the strategic future for Dounreay. In the RWMAC's view, the heated debate which accompanied receipt at Dounreay of the Georgian highly-enriched uranium was generated not by reprocessing per se, but by concerns about the import into the UK of a material which some people perceived as a very hazardous waste.

Supporters of reprocessing argue that Dounreay offers expertise to engage in the management and processing of radioactive materials and wastes for which there is likely to be a significant world-wide demand in the future, and should receive investment to sustain its role in reprocessing. By contrast, opponents fear that further investment in reprocessing could lead, incrementally, to an escalation of the role of Dounreay as a focus for the import and export of nuclear materials and the consequential long-term management of foreign fuels and wastes.

As an indication of the degree of polarisation, the RWMAC notes that in 1995, the Electoral Reform Society organised a further referendum, funded by Caithness Against Nuclear Dumping, among electors in the Caithness District Council area on a hypothetical proposal that further foreign fuel might be reprocessed at Dounreay. The question was "The USA is due to make a decision soon on what should happen to nuclear fuel elements it supplied to research reactors in 33 different countries. One suggestion is that many of the used nuclear fuel elements be brought from abroad to Dounreay for reprocessing. Are you in favour of this proposal?" In a 53 per cent turnout, 65.5 per cent voted against and 34.5 per cent voted in favour.

The decommissioning and waste management programme means that immediate employment prospects for Dounreay are secure. At present, there are around 1400 people employed at the plant. This number would be likely to remain, even without any further reprocessing, for at least a decade with a slow decline thereafter. This would provide ample time for planning for change and diversification in activities at Dounreay.

Appendices
Appendix 19

Apprenticeships and Training Schemes.

Dounreay provided an immense opportunity not only for work for the people of the area but for the constructive development of their skills and knowledge.

A decision was taken by UKAEA in 1955 to set up an engineering craft apprenticeship scheme. UKAEA was keen to ensure that as the site expanded there was a pool of skilled labour available and, right from the start, apprentices were required to study. Initially this was undertaken at temporary accommodation in Thurso and then at Robert Gordon's Technical College (now University) in Aberdeen.

UKAEA also took a strong interest in the health and physical well-being of the apprentices. They encouraged physical training and, in the early days, utilised the experience of Johnny Duffus, a UKAEA employee who was a former physical training instructor. When the first purpose-built training centre opened in 1960 it incorporated a small gymnasium.

From that initial intake of eleven apprentices in 1955, the scheme developed until the number reached an average of 35 new recruits annually and, to ensure that UKAEA attracted the best, the recruitment area was expanded to include much of the Highlands including Orkney and Shetland. A 70-bed hostel, Naver House, was built in 1962 within the Pennyland housing estate in Thurso, to accommodate the numbers involved.

And in the mid-seventies, the traditional male-dominated apprentice scheme welcomed its first lady when Catherine Rosie, a Thurso girl, joined the scheme.

When talk of closure of the fast reactor programme was in the air at the back-end of the eighties, UKAEA decided that, as its apprenticeship scheme was the only one of significance in the north of Scotland and that there would be a continued need for skilled engineers, it would continue with its programme although reduce the intake numbers.

However, in 2003 reflecting the change from operations to shutdown, Dounreay launched Britain's first modern apprenticeships in nuclear operations and decommissioning. Today, this scheme is integrated into the engineering apprenticeship.

Quite properly, Dounreay takes a considerable pride in its apprenticeship schemes and its apprentices and the manner in which the scheme has enriched the lives of so many.

The Dounreay Clerical and Secretarial Training Scheme was established in 1960. Its purpose was two-fold, to provide a social need and to act as a source of trained administrators for the expanding site.

The first intake was of twelve people, six clerical and six secretarial. At the start, their training centre was a wooden hut adjacent to the canteen. The first instructors, Joe Byrne and Jean Hannah, taught the rudiments of administration and typing. The trainees were also expected to attend courses in Thurso Technical College where a rapidly expanding curriculum was on offer.

However, in 2004, with the decommissioning programme taking shape and a much different administrative structure required, the decision was taken to end this training scheme. The scheme had lasted all of 44 years and seen 564 young people take advantage of it.

In 1965, UKAEA launched a scientific training scheme to supplement and complement its apprenticeship and clerical schemes. The work being carried out required virtually every scientific discipline and a structured training programme was adopted whereby trainees spent four three month placements on different parts of the site during their first year. This provided a broad overview into the diverse work but it also acted as a stimulus for an individual to decide what particular subject was most attractive to them. It was a requirement of their employment that they attend college to gain nationally recognised certificates and diplomas.

With the closure of PFR and the gradual cessation of work in fuel reprocessing, the need for such training started to diminish. The intake of 1999 was the final year for a scheme that had seen 220 scientific trainees pass through it.

Dounreay was also active In the Youth Training Scheme (YTS) that the government introduced in 1983. This non-craft scheme was designed to introduce young people to the workplace and to gain work experience through a structured programme. Dounreay became a managing agent for the scheme. This ceased in 1993 but not before 213 individuals had passed through Dounreay's YTS scheme.

Appendices
Appendix 20

Safety and Dounreay.

From its inception, Dounreay had inherited a well-developed system of safety management that had been worked out within the UKAEA. It was based on two fundamental principles:-

1) The operator is responsible and liable for the safety of his operations and the consequences of accidents.

2) The operator is required to maintain the risk of all such accidents (and of untoward occurrences) at levels as "low as reasonably practicable."

These principles continue to be at the heart of the safety strategy. Their mode of implementation has changed considerably over time. The most significant changes occurred from November 1990 when the site became licensed under the Nuclear Installations Act. The other marked change, perhaps even more marked, happened two years later when the Authority's own management structure altered drastically.

Until at least that time, the safety organisation of Dounreay had been based on three precepts, viz:-

1) The overall responsibility for safety in all its aspects, whether statutory or otherwise, was vested in the head of the establishment.

2) All branch, divisional and equivalent were responsible to the head of the establishment for safety within their individual areas of activity, irrespective of the existence of other managerial reporting chains.

3) Each departmental manager was responsible for having in place, within his area of activity, an effective safety management system such as to ensure that his own and the establishment head's safety responsibilities were adequately met.

In the early days, although the existence of such a safety structure was an essential condition, it was not formally described in writing, although it was implicit in directives given. It is also implied in the Authority's early general notices on the safety organisation. The desirability (later a statutory requirement) of keeping communities in the local area informed of safety related matters was also recognised and, from November 1957, this was achieved through the Dounreay Local Liaison Committee. A national joint committee on health and safety (JCHS), supported by similar local committees at the various UKAEA sites had already been established prior to the inception of Dounreay. Thus a Dounreay JCHS was swiftly established as well. With the promulgation of the safety representatives and Safety Committees Regulations in 1977, the Dounreay JCHS became the site's statutory committee.

There were already procedures in place, when Dounreay opened, for the safety clearance of plant. In particular there was a requirement for appropriate safety documentation concerning the loading of fuel and the subsequent operation of reactors and critical assemblies. Further safety related documentation was required before experimental work could be undertaken on such plant.

The safety approval of operations, modifications and new equipment on DFR and DMTR and for all other critical assembly work became a site matter in 1957 and continued with the setting up of the Dounreay Reactor Safety Committee in 1959. Later, in the 1970s, a "Safety Approval of Modifications" system was introduced and this became progressively more rigorous over the years. Another safety related discipline, first introduced on PFR, was the "Maintenance, Inspection and Test System" used primarily during periodic inspections and overhauls.

Also, into the 1960s, a number of localised, plant-based area safety committees were set up. Each of these concerned itself with all matters affecting the general day-to-day household safety, both radiological and non-radiological, of persons and plant within the stated area.

As the numbers of permanent staff on site increased and pressure intensified as reactors, plants and laboratories came into full operation, more stress was placed on this system. At the same time the Fleck report on the Windscale accident was published with its far-reaching recommendations. This all led, gradually, to a more formal safety system. By the time the decision was announced to build the Prototype Fast Reactor (PFR), a PFR safety working party had been in place for some years. In contrast to the pioneering days of DFR, there were many individuals who had operational and experimental experience gained on DFR who could contribute significantly to PFR safety procedures.

The latter half of the 1960s also saw the development of a comprehensive system of technical safety committees, termed safety working parties, covering virtually all plant and activities on the Dounreay site. An important development occurred in 1977 with the formation of the safety of environmental discharges working party (SEDWP). This was a body with site-wide responsibilities whose terms of reference required it to consider the nature and impact on the environment of actual and potential discharges from any plant or caused by any operations on the Dounreay site. Although initially set up to consider radioactive discharges, the remit for this body eventually extended to encompass all forms of effluent discharge as well as the disposal and storage, on or off site, of solid waste.

The next major change happened in the late 1980s and was a consequence of UKAEA coming into the scope of the Nuclear Installations Act of 1965. It was a condition of this that the director, as site licence holder, had to be advised by a nuclear safety committee (NSC) and this was duly organised. The safety committee structure was replaced in 1992 when, by that date, the Authority had adopted what was considered a business structure whereby the chief executives of the several businesses assumed responsibility for all operations under their control. This negated the position and need for a site director and that post then ceased to exist.

When Dounreay commenced, the only formalised arrangements for reporting and investigation of incidents, which existed within the UKAEA, were some very general instructions inherited from the Ministry of Supply. These were mainly concerned with major incidents and did not cover minor accidents.

There was no Authority-wide system for classifying incidents, either by type or severity, and none existed at Dounreay although some elementary classification schemes were in use at some other UKAEA establishments. A considerably greater degree of formality was introduced following the infamous Windscale fire. Even before the Windscale report was published, expanded rules on the notification of major accidents had been issued including a standardized classification system.

A consequence of that Windscale fire was that there commenced a routine exchange of summarised information on incidents between the sites, either under the aegis of the newly formed health physics co-ordination committee or directly between plant management. Systematic recording of "incidents and unusual occurrences" began at Dounreay in 1962 and formalised further in the following year with the adoption of a standardised report form. This ran in parallel with the development of a system for recording radiological incidents as well as some non-radiological ones by the health and safety division.

Since that time, arrangements for reporting incidents have developed and formalised considerably, particularly with the legal requirement to report certain incidents to the Nuclear Installations Inspectorate – a legal requirement brought in from 1977 onwards. In 1982 these arrangements were widened with a further requirement that all incidents of certain significance were also to be reported to the appropriate government departments and their ministers.

In 1987 these arrangements were extended requiring nuclear operators to record in a site log all incidents whether formally reportable or not and these were published weekly and given wide circulation outside the industry as well as within. Later the industry reported to the International Atomic Energy authority on events each of which was assigned a severity rating of events, below zero (minor) to 7 (Chernobyl type).

Appendices
Appendix 21– List of Directors

Major-General SW Joslin *   1956-1958

Dr Robert Hurst   1958-1963

Dr Roy Matthews   1963-1968

Mr Peter Mummery   1968-1974

Mr Clifford Blumfield   1975-1987

Mr Gerry Jordan   1987-1992**

Mr John Baxter   **1994-1996

Dr Roy Nelson, OBE   1996-1999

Mr Peter Welsh, OBE   1998-2003

Mr Norman Harrison   2003-2007

Mr Simon Middlemas   2007-

* Major-General Joslin,
who oversaw the early
construction of the site, was
designated Works General
Manager.

**Between 1992 and
1994, UKAEA's various
functions were split up
and relocated among the
Authority's sites, with only
Fuel Services Division
having its headquarters
at Dounreay. There
was no designated site
director at Dounreay.

The Prototype Fast Reactor.